THE BEGINNING

Creation Myths around the World

BY MARIA LEACH

ILLUSTRATIONS BY JAN BELL FAIRSERVIS

FUNK & WAGNALLS COMPANY

NEW YORK   *1956*

1

THE BEGINNING

. . the earth swings free,
*   held in its place by nothing . .*

— ANAXIMANDER

CONTENTS

7

8

9

11

I
Introduction

At Nine O'Clock in the Morning and Other Tales

THE *Old Farmer's Almanac* says that the world began at nine o'clock in the morning on Wednesday, October 26 in the year 4004 B.C. This is the famous date worked out by James Ussher, Archbishop of Armagh in Ireland, from his studies of ancient Hebrew chronology.

But astronomers today know that the earth is much older than that. Today we think that the earth was born about six billion years ago, and (as in some of the old myths) that it is the child of the sun.

The life-giving power of the sun caused the ancient Egyptians to cast the sun god in the role of creator. The Incas of Peru thought of the sun as the beneficent father who rose up out of Lake Titicaca and created the world and the Incas. The North American Zuni Indians thought of the sun as the father of mankind. The Yuchi said the sun was "the mother," and called themselves People of the Sun. The Yahao Chins of Burma believed that mankind (i.e. they themselves) were hatched from an egg laid by the sun.

We think today that somehow the earth and the other eight planets "broke off" from the parent sun and evolved their own independent wandering lives. And we are reminded that the old men of the Zulu people in South Africa told their young men the story of Unkulunkulu and how the earth, and mankind too, "broke off" from the primeval bed of reeds which was the source of everything. The old Greek philosopher Anaxagoras (*c.* 500-428 B.C.) was the first to say that the heavenly bodies broke off (i.e. were thrown off) by some central revolving mass of red-hot matter.

But as the ages passed men wanted to *prove* that the earth was born of the sun. So they made a test. Through that magical thing called a prism, which breaks up light into the colors of the rainbow, they looked at the "rainbow of the sun." The rainbow of the sun is its chromosphere, a gaseous layer surrounding it and containing incandescent particles of all the elements. The test was made by English scientists in India in 1868 during a total eclipse of the sun. And when they examined the chromosphere of the sun, they found that it contained all the same elements known on earth, plus one more, which they named *helium*, from the Greek word *helios*, which means sun. Later, in 1895, when helium was discovered to be an element of this earth also, this seemed to clinch the sun-parent theory.

The origin of the earth has preoccupied the mind of man since the beginning of time. It was natural for him to believe that his wonderful world was the center of the universe, that the sun and moon rose and set for its sake, and that sun, moon, and stars revolved around it.

Then, in 1543, the Polish scientist Copernicus upset the old thinking. The sun is the center, he said; the earth is not the whole show; it is one of the planets and all together revolve around the sun. Then, in 1610, Galileo looked through his telescope and said yes, Copernicus was right. Later came Isaac Newton who discovered and proved the law of gravitation, and later yet came Albert Einstein who disproved it with his doctrine of relativity. Still later the Abbé Georges Lemaître, basing his argument on Einstein's findings, came up with the theory of the expanding universe. The galaxies in space are all rushing *away from*—not toward—each other, he said, at the terrific speed of thousands of miles per second.

Many wonderful and strange stories about the beginning of the world have come out of the search for truth on the part of the astronomers, physicists, and geologists, and are still coming. Some of these tales are about: (1) the nebular hypothesis; (2) the eruption or planetesimal theory; (3) the tidal theory; (4) the collision theory; (5) the catastrophic theory or the story of the big blow-up; (6) the tale of the lonely atoms or the continuous creation theory.

Nebular Hypothesis. The nebular hypothesis presents the idea that the whole solar system was once one huge rotating nebula (i.e. a vast, luminous, gaseous celestial body) which, cooling and contracting, gradually in-

17

creased the speed of its rotation and, whirling faster and faster, by the centrifugal force of this rotation, threw off great revolving rings of gaseous matter, that, likewise cooling and shrinking, became the planets. This nebular hypothesis was advanced by the French scientist, the Marquis Pierre Simon de Laplace in 1796, and was quite generally accepted until about 1900.

Eruption Theory. The planetesimal or eruption theory was advanced by two American scientists, the astronomer Forest Ray Moulton and the geologist Thomas C. Chamberlin, about 1905. They said that long ages ago some big star passed by our sun in space near enough to exert such terrific attraction on the fluid mass (which the sun was) that huge tidal bulges were raised on it—one toward the passing star and one in the opposite direction. Violent eruptions characteristically took place in the two tidal bulges. Then as the passing stranger swung off into its own orbit, the debris erupting from the two bulges was set in motion in elliptical orbits around the sun and held in those orbits by the cross-pull between the bulges. Some of the debris dropped back into the sun's mass; some of it erupted with such speed and force that it shot off into space and was lost; some of it became the nine planets we know, which are still revolving around the sun. And one of the nine is *us*. Our shooting stars (meteors) are thought to be fragments of left-over debris from this violent event.

Tidal Theory. The tidal theory was advanced in 1918 by Sir James Jeans. He too believed that a wandering star passed by the sun and that its attraction raised mountainous tides on the sun's surface. The pull was so strong that the crest of the huge tidal wave was pulled away into an elongated cigar-shaped mass. This in turn was torn to shreds and the shreds dashed off into space, just as any crested wave scatters spray. These shreds are the nine planets, which now circle around the sun. Thus, in this theory, the earth was first a flaming, whirling ball, a fiery shred of the sun let loose in space, and as it cooled it put on—in something like two to four billion years—the solid crust we walk upon. It looks big and important to us, but in space, among the uncountable millions of stars, it rides in its own place, as little, in comparison, as one grain of sand in all the sand at the edge of all the seas.

Collision Theory. The collision theory proposed that some huge wandering star sideswiped the sun and tore off the pieces which became the planets. This is an earlier theory, revived by the English scientist Harold Jeffreys, when certain aspects of the tidal theory seemed untenable to the astronomers.

Catastrophic Theory. The world was created in about fifteen minutes, according to the catastrophic theory, in one big blow-up ages ago. With this huge explosion the solar system was set in its present routine and has been expanding ever since. (This is Lemaître's proposition; see page 15.) Many scientists believe that this is what really happened. But what the state of affairs was before that big bang no one can guess.

Continuous Creation Theory. Another story that many scientists believe is the one that explains the theory of continuous creation: the story of the lonely atoms. *The universe is still being created*, say the cosmologists of Cambridge, England. Way off in space, in each several million cubic feet of space ONE lonely atom of hydrogen is created every year; and out of these hydrogen atoms they say the whole universe has evolved. Gravitation pulls the hydrogen atoms together until they form into nebulae and stars and galaxies. Then the law of gravitation ceases to work and they go tearing off into space away from each other. Then more hydrogen is created in the emptiness and the story begins all over again.

Nobody knows for sure which tale is really true. And who knows but what the scientists may have a brand new thriller for us to read in the morning?

But whatever the story, it is true that some billions of years ago this, our beautiful earth, BECAME. In time it made itself a crust. Oceans collected in the holes of that crust and the gases which swirled around it would have looked like haze to some prehistoric gazer on Mars. More than one myth mentions the primeval haze or fog. The story *Ancient Matters* from Japan is one of them; and in the Zuni Indian *From-the-Beginning-Talk* the sun's rays had to roll away the mists that enveloped the earth before mankind could emerge.

Space is so cold that no life can exist in it. Most of the stars are so hot that there can be no life in or very near them. *Who am I*, says man, *to receive life on this grain of sand called Earth?*

How long were the oceans there before there was a fish? How long was the face of the earth bare rock before the soft soil lay upon it? How long before the tall primeval grasses took hold? How many millions of years before some courageous "crawler" ventured ashore out of the sea

20

and took a breath of air? Evolution says that all life began in the ocean and that the two-legged man (who now has learned to search space and ocean for his answers) originated in that prehistoric adventurer from the sea who dared to crawl ashore! And how long did man walk on earth before he was suddenly aware of the unanswerable sky and the spirit within himself?

How did this world begin?
Who am I?

The sixty-two stories in this book give only a few of the answers man has told himself in his ardent search for truth. There are hundreds more such tales in the world. They do not tell us anything about the history of the peoples who tell them; but they do reveal the mind of man. These stories represent the imagination of all humanity. They represent the quest for reality behind the mystery of the spheres, sun, moon, and stars, and of outer space, the mystery of rotation, and the staggering mystery of life and of man himself.

The answers to the questions man asks himself take the form of myth and story. It does not matter that all the answers are not true. A wrong answer does not belittle the seeking for an answer.

It is interesting to note how many peoples, without contact or knowledge of each other, have come up with some of the same conjectures. And it is exciting how close these conjectures are, *sometimes*, to the story of geology and evolution, coming as they do from peoples who never heard those words.

Some of the concepts are practically world-wide: as, for instance, the idea that the universe began with chaos or the primeval water; and some occur only once, perhaps, or are limited to a certain locality, as the story of Raven calling to mankind to come out of the clamshell.

Primitive man had observed the mystery of rotation and explained it in various ways. Roll Over, said the Pomo Indian creator, in order to establish the succession of day and night. Earthmaker of the Winnebago Indians hurled his world off into space and it went spinning and turning so fast that only with effort could it be slowed down enough to assume the quiet of a summer day.

But here are stories about a world being shaped and hewn by a creator, or being made from parts of a creator's body. Here is a universe materializing at the utterance of a creative word, or evolving by itself out of nothingness, or from the green slime or scum on the primeval water. Here are a few of the earth-diver stories: the earth being created from a tiny bit of mud brought up from the bottom of the primeval sea by some courageous animal or water-bird. Here are a few of the ancient supreme gods, grand and benevolent and far away. And here are a few of the creator worms from South America and Micronesia, where worm outnumbers man.

Here is man emerging from his mother the earth, or from a tree, or a rock, or a clamshell. Here is man descended from the gods, the divine spark taken for granted, or created from earth or clay and animated by the god with the god's own breath, the breath of life, or by drumming, or by the dance of life. Here are some stories about man being made in the image of the creator, or evolving from the germ of the world itself, his kinship

22

to some ancestral reptile form strangely recognized, especially in the lizard stories.

Following are a few of the concepts of the creation of the world and of mankind found in the stories in this book. The numbers preceding each concept are the motif numbers of these concepts in Stith Thompson's *Motif-Index of World-Literature*. They are included for those who may want to continue their interest by further reading. Where no number is given, that particular concept does not appear in the *Motif-Index*. Following each concept are the titles of the stories in this book which contain it.

I CREATORS

A1   sun god as creator
          The First Time; Sun-Papa; Followers of the Golden Rod; Who?

A12.1   male and female creators
          Ancient Matters

A13.1   raven as creator
          Raven Finds a Clam; That Is All

A14   cow as creator
          Middangeard
          lizard as creator
          Lizard Hand; Lizard's People
          worm as creator
          Mbir; About the Little Islands
          creator discovered himself
          Our Great Father; It Was Turning

A22   creator comes out of chaos
          The First Time; Something from Nothing

A60   marplot as creator's companion
          The Mountains and the Valleys; Our Great Father; First Noses; In Melanesia; Qat; Dream Time

24

The First Time; The Heartless People; Ancient and Original Sayings; Mmmmmm

A614   creation of universe from parts of creator's body
       Roll Over; First Noses; Something from Nothing

       creation of universe from parts of a deity's body
       Earth-Woman; About the Little Islands; Middangeard

A617   creation of universe from mussel shell (or clamshell)
       About the Little Islands

A620
&
A620.1   spontaneous creation (the world evolved)
       Nobody There; Beginning-in-Deep-Darkness; Lord of Creatures

       earth from primeval scum or slime
       In the Day of Obscurity; Beginning-in-Deep-Darkness; The First Time

       earth made in the form of a raft supported by spirits
       The Worm Turned

       all creation (god, world, and man) broke off from the bed of reeds
       Unkulunkulu

A641   universe brought forth from cosmic egg
       The First Time; Something from Nothing; Lord of Creatures

A641.1   heaven and earth from egg (from two halves of eggshell)
       Barley Grow

A642   universe from body of slain giant
       Middangeard

A651   series of worlds, one above the other
       See Aztec cosmos: vertical; See Yami cosmos

A700.2   universe, man, and living creatures vomited by creator

25

III MAN

A1220.1	mankind created after series of unsuccessful attempts
	To Live in Happiness; The Heartless People; A Better Lot
A1225	first men undeveloped
	From-the-Beginning-Talk; Lizard's People
A1232	mankind emerges from the earth
	From-the-Beginning-Talk; Man Emerges
A1232.3	mankind emerges from caves
	Followers of the Golden Rod
	mankind emerges from rocks
	It Was There
	mankind emerges from clamshell
	Raven Finds a Clam
A1236	mankind emerges from a tree
	Old Man; In the Day of Obscurity; The Outbursters; In Melanesia
A1241	man made from earth or clay
	Earth-Woman; It Was Turning; Modern Seneca Folktale of Creation; Followers of the Golden Rod; The Worm Turned; Mbere's Man; Ancient and Original Sayings; The Fur Coat; The First Time; Out of Chaos; Qat
A1241.3	man made from earth or clay and vivified
	Earth Woman; It Was Turning; Ancient and Original Sayings; Qat
	first man born of a stone
	The Outbursters; Qat
A1245	man created from stones (pebbles)
	That Is All
A1251	first man made from a tree
	Middangeard
	man created from slips of a tree
	To Live in Happiness
A1255.2	man created from ears of corn
	A Better Lot

A1263.3   man created from rubbings of creator's skin
                 Roll Over; First Noses
           man created by wishing
                 To Live in Happiness
A1311.1   lizard hand
                 The Lizard Hand
           man made in lizard form
                 The Lizard Hand; Mbere's Man; Hello, I'm
                 a Lizard; Lizard's People
           man made in image of the creator
                 Fit to Live; It Was Turning; Modern Sen-
                 eca Folktales of Creation; First Noses
           mankind discovered by animal
                 Chameleon Finds; Man Emerges
A1335   origin of death
                 Lizard Hand; Ancient and Original Sayings;
                 Qat; Mmmmmm; Dream Time; Hello, I'm a
                 Lizard; Ancient Matters

28

II

The Mountains and the Valleys

THE MOUNTAINS
AND THE VALLEYS

IN THE BEGINNING, when God finished making the heavens, he took a little ball of thread and measured them. Then he started to create the earth to fit under them.

The mole came along and said, "Let me help." And God, who is good, said, "All right," and gave him the ball of thread to hold.

So God set to work, weaving the earth. Once in a while the mole would let out a little more thread than God had measured off. But God didn't notice; he just went on weaving and shaping the earth. Then when it was finished, he was amazed to see that the earth was too big—too big to fit under the heavens.

He started to exclaim to the mole, but the mole was not there. He was afraid and had buried himself in the earth.

God walked around looking for him but did not see him anywhere. So he sent the bee to search out the mole and ask his advice.

It did not take the clever bee very long to spy the hole where the mole was hiding.

"Good morning," said the bee.

"What do you want?" said the mole.

"God says, 'What's to be done?'" said the bee, "for the earth is too big."

The mole just laughed. "God knows," he said. "I'm not telling *Him!*"

So the bee did not ask again. She pretended to fly away, but hid in a flower near by, hoping the mole would say something.

The mole had nobody to talk to, so he talked to himself.

"Well, if *I* had to do it," he mused, "I would take the earth up and squeeze it, so that mountains would stick up and valleys would sink down, and the earth would be smaller."

The bee heard this, and buzzed off in a hurry. The mole heard the buzzing and called out, "That's a fine trick to play! My curse on you! Henceforth, feed on yourself."

The bee flew straight to God and told him what the mole had said. And God took hold of the wide flat earth and squeezed it. Mountains rose up into folds and valleys sank into deep clefts, till the earth fitted nicely under the heavens, the way God had measured.

As for the bee, God said, "Let the curse be a blessing." So now the bee makes honey for itself, and the mole lives underground and is afraid to come out.

Rewritten from Moses Gaster: *Rumanian Bird and Beast Stories.*

III

North American Indian

ROLL OVER

THIS is the tale of the old men, the tale of world-making, of making the people. This is the tale I was told.

He lived in the north, did Old Man Madumda, and he thought, "I will make the world."

"How shall I make it?" he thought. "I'll ask my elder brother."

He pulled out four hairs from his head and held them up. "Take me to my brother," he said. He held the hairs to the east; nothing happened. He held the hairs to the north. No. He held them to the west; nothing happened. He held the hairs to the south. The hairs floated. They floated in a circle around Madumda and then started swiftly south. They flashed fire as they flew and Madumda followed, riding in his cloud-house. He smoked his pipe or slept as he traveled, and finally he got there. He arrived at the house of Kuksu, his elder brother.

Four times the hairs swished around the house of Kuksu, then floated in through a little hole, and Madumda followed and entered the house of his brother.

Madumda sat down and smoked his pipe. Four times he put the pipe in his mouth and then passed it to Kuksu. Kuksu took the pipe and smoked it.

"Good will come of this," he said. "It will happen."

Then Madumda scratched off some skin from under his armpit and rolled it into a little ball, which he handed to Kuksu. Kuksu placed it between his big toe and the next. Then Kuksu scraped himself under the armpit and rolled the dead skin into a little ball, which he placed between Madumda's big toe and the next. Madumda then took the ball in his hand and blew upon it four times, and Kuksu also blew four times upon the little ball of skin which Madumda had given him.

Then the brothers took the two little balls and molded them together into one. Kuksu took some of his own hair to mix into it and Madumda did the same.

Then they stood up and turned, facing the six sacred directions: first south, then east, then north, then west, then into the zenith, then down to the nadir.

"Thus everything will be," they said. "There will be people on this earth; there will be food; there will be villages. The people will be many and full of good intentions.

"We shall make the sun, to ripen the food," they said.

"We shall give them fire to cook it."

"This is a good plan," said Kuksu. "All will be good."

Then Madumda put the little ball of dried skin into a sack and said he must go.

"Sing your song," he said to Kuksu. And Kuksu sang the long, holy song in the ancient language which nobody understands today. Then Madumda floated homeward to the north, singing his own wishing-song in that old language.

Singing, he tied a string to the little ball which he and Kuksu had made, and strung it through his ear-hole, so that he would not lose it when he went to sleep. For now Madumda slept.

Eight days he slept. He would sleep, wake up, look, see nothing, and go back to sleep. On the eighth day the string jerked and Madumda woke. The little ball had grown big and become the earth.

AND MADUMDA HURLED IT OUT INTO SPACE.

It was dark, so Madumda made the sun. He lighted his pipe and when it was afire he blew the glowing spark into the southern sky. And the spark grew big and became the sun and shed its lovely light over the face of the earth.

Then Madumda walked around in the world, fixing things. "Here a mountain, here some rocks," he said. "Now a valley, a lake, clover growing, acorns on the mountains, juniper and cherries. There must be potatoes and rabbits," he said, "and on that mountain over there, let there be bear, puma, wolf, coyote, fox, skunk; on this one rattlesnakes, kingsnakes, garter snakes."

Then Madumda climbed a mountain and on the other

side of the mountain it was dark. "Well!" he said. He sat down to think. There was no light here at all. He looked up, and there was light in the sky.

"ROLL OVER," he said to the earth. Madumda turned it over, then turned it back. He rolled the earth over, first one side to the sun, then the other.

"This is the way," he said. "Now it is dark, now it is light; now dark, now light. This is the way." And so it is.

Madumda continued his work. He made rivers, to be roads for the fish; he made a mountain of flint to be arrowheads for the people; he made springs. He planted rushes and bushes, dogwood and willows. "These shall be for the women to weave baskets," he said.

Madumda walked around and came to a lake, and sat down on a log. The lake was calm and smooth. "Don't be like that," said Madumda, "be like this," and he walked into the water and splashed it toward the land. The wind blew and made ripples in the water and the waves ran up on the land and splashed on the rocks.

"That's nice," said Madumda. "That's the way."

Then Madumda thought it was time to make the people. He picked up a few rocks and made some people. They were little short-legged people and stayed in the mountains. Then he made some people out of hair. These had beautiful long black hair. Madumda ate some potatoes to show them how. "This is your food," he said.

Madumda went on and made more people in another place. He made them out of feathers and scattered them all over. These people were covered with feathers. They were bird-people.

Then Madumda pulled four hairs out from under his

arm and made some more people. These were covered with hair and had horns on their heads and split hooves. They were deer-people.

Madumda went on and sat on a hill. He took some more hair and scattered it over the hills to make another kind of people. These were big, hairy people with claws, walking about on four legs. They were bear-people. "Are there others besides ourselves?" they asked their maker. "Oh, yes, there will be lots of people," said Madumda. Then he showed them how to eat and went on his way.

Madumda walked northward into the hills and sat down. He reached into his sack and took out some sinew. This he broke into little pieces and scattered the pieces in the hollow between the hills.

"These shall be naked people," he said.

And they were. They were like us. They had hair on their heads but no horns, no feathers or hair on their bodies. They were beautiful and naked and slick in the sunshine.

"Come here," said Madumda, and the people came and listened. "This is your land," said Madumda. "This is where you will live. There is plenty of food. Eat it." He spoke thus and went away.

All these were the first people that Madumda made.

This story and the next one, "To Live in Happiness," both of the Pomo Indians of California, are here retold and condensed from the Pomo creation myth as reported by J. de Angulu in *Journal of American Folklore*, vol. 48, 203-262 (1935). A. L. Kroeber: *Handbook of the Indians of California* spells the name of the Pomo supreme god as Madumda.

TO LIVE IN HAPPINESS

TIME PASSED, time passed, time passed, time passed. And when Madumda looked at the world he saw that the people were behaving very badly. They were killing each other and fighting and the children were not growing up strong and healthy.

"I'd better wash them away," said Madumda. So he smoked to the four directions. The thunder rolled; the skies grew dark; rain fell. The rain became a flood and Madumda himself had to scramble and run among the rocks till he came to a mountain peak.

When it was over the people were all washed away. Not one was left. Madumda called. No one answered.

"There should be a village here," said Madumda. And thus, for his wishing, the village appeared.

"These will be good people," said Madumda, "healthy, playful. They will be kind," he said.

Madumda called again and the people came pouring out of the houses: young boys and girls, men, children, women. They ran here and there, laughing; the boys played tag in the lake; the people bathed and splashed and shouted. These were the people Madumda wished into existence.

"Claim strangers as your friends," he told them. Then Madumda went away.

Time passed, time passed, time passed, time passed. And Madumda looked into the world and saw that these people too had fallen into evil ways.

"I'll have to burn them," he said. So Madumda destroyed this second creation by fire.

"But there must be people," said Madumda. "All that I have in mind must come true."

This time he made the people out of willow wands. He cut the young, green willow wands and stuck them upright in the earth. The next day they were people, tall and straight and active.

Madumda showed them how to make bows and arrows, how to hunt the deer, how to weave baskets and fishtraps out of willow roots, how to make mush out of acorns. Then Madumda disappeared and went to his home in the north.

Time passed, time passed, time passed, time passed. Madumda looked into the world and could not believe what he saw. Again the people were doing wrong things.

"Why do they act like this?" he said. "What is the

43

matter with the world?"

This time Madumda destroyed the people with ice and snow. They all froze to death. Then Madumda waited and slept a long time, and when he went back to walk around the world, only the birds were there.

Once again Madumda created the people; once again he made them out of willow wands. Again he told them everything they ought to do, this time showing them also how to roll milkweed into string and weave fishnets. This time he made two villages and told the people they were brothers. "Visit each other," he said. "Eat together. Share your food."

Thus spoke Madumda and went away, and the people did not see him any more.

Time passed, time passed, time passed, time passed. Madumda saw the people in a dream, doing wrong. He looked down to see what was going on.

"They have thrown away their knowledge," he said, lamenting.

So he decided to consult with his elder brother, Kuksu. He arrived; the brothers smoked. Four times Madumda inhaled and passed the pipe to Kuksu; four times Kuksu inhaled and returned the pipe to Madumda.

"Again they have been doing wrong, those people," said Madumda. "I want your consent to destroy them for the last time."

"This time you had better blow them away with a whirlwind," said Kuksu, "so that the next people cannot inherit their badness from the bones in the ground."

"You are right," said Madumda. "I shall blow away the world, and then we shall make a new people."

So Whirlwind whirled and the waters stood on end and the trees were uprooted, and the people were blown off the face of the earth.

Ground-Squirrel poked his head up out of his hole to see what was going on. Whirlwind almost got him, but Ground-Squirrel scooted back underground.

When it was over and the world was clean, Madumda once again began to make the people. "These shall speak different languages," he said.

Once again he took the lithe willow wands and set them on end in the ground, and went to sleep. When he woke up, already they were people. Madumda woke and heard them talking among themselves.

They saw Madumda. "Who are you?" they said. "I have come to look at the village and teach the people," he answered.

Once again Madumda went through the long days of teaching the people how to live, how to make bows and tip their arrows with flint, how to hunt deer, weave baskets, prepare acorns, fish with nets and traps, dam rivers, make canoes, and pound seeds and acorns with the *metate* (grinding stone).

"Live righteously and be healthy," Madumda said, and walked on around the world, telling the people what to do.

When he came back to this first village, "Where have you been?" the people said. "Not far, not far," Madumda answered, "around the world. Not far."

"Are there other people?"

"Yes. Lots of other people," Madumda said. "Be friends with them."

Then Madumda taught the people their dances and

45

ceremonies, how to prepare feasts and hold festivals, and how to sing their sacred songs and perform the four-day dance.

"Take care of each other," he told them all. "Live in happiness."

Then Madumda walked about in the mountains and called together the coyotes. "You watch over the villages," he told them; "if enemies approach, cry out." And so the coyotes did for years and years. They cried out when strangers approached a village, and the people heard and understood.

Then Madumda called together the wolves, the lynxes, pumas, foxes, raccoons, squirrels, martens, and the bears, and told each kind where to live and where to find his food. He called together the elk and the deer, and told them to live in the hills.

He told the rabbits, the moles, gophers, mice, and badgers that it would be nice to live in holes underground. He called together the rattlesnakes and big and little snakes, the lizards, and the snails, and told them how best to get along in the world. He instructed the birds in all their ways.

He called the fish out of the water to tell them how to live. Turtle came ashore first, and behind him came all the fishes.

"*You're* not a fish!" said Madumda to Turtle. "But you can catch your food in the water if you want to. Now, you fish," he said, "must not come ashore. Live in the water."

And so Madumda's work was done and he disappeared. "Hold together," he told the world, for the last time.

SEDNA

The Eskimo around Frobisher Bay, the Nugumiut, used to tell about a high god named Anguta. (The word *anguta* means "his father.") He made the earth, the sky, and the sea, and put the stars in their places. The story does not say how, only that this was done.

The most widespread story told by the Central Eskimo of northeastern America was picked up by the famous anthropologist, Dr. Franz Boas, among the Oqomiut of Cumberland Sound and the Akudnirmiut of Hudson Strait. This is the Sedna story, which is more concerned with the creation of mankind and living creatures important to man than with the creation of the world. The world was there.

LONG AGO an Inung lived with his daughter Sedna on a lonely northern shore. (*Inung* is the word for man among the Central Eskimo.) Sedna was very beautiful and many a young man came to woo her, but she did not want any of them.

47

One spring when the ice was breaking up a great fulmar flew in over the ice and sang to Sedna.

> "*Come with me,*" he sang.
> "*Come to the land of birds where no hunger is.*
> *My tent is made of beautiful skins.*
> *You shall sleep on a bearskin.*
> *Your garments shall be the softest fulmar*
> *feathers.*
> *Your lamp will never go out.*
> *Your lamp shall be filled with oil.*
> *Your kettle will be full of meat.*"

Sedna was charmed with the song and went with the fulmar over the sea. But when they arrived, she was horrified to see that the fulmar's tent was a ragged tent of fishskins. The wind howled in through the cracks and holes. There was no bearskin to sleep on—nothing but a tough old walrus hide. There was no meat. The birds fed her nothing but fish.

> "*O, father,*" she sang.
> "*Come with your boat.*
> *I am a stranger among strange birds.*
> *I sleep under the whistling wind.*
> *I eat fish.*
> *O, father, come with your boat.*"

At the end of a year, when the warm winds blew over the sea and the ice broke up, the father came in his boat to visit his daughter. When he saw how things were, he killed the fulmar, put Sedna into his boat, and started home.

Soon all the fulmars came home from their fishing and

48

found the murdered body of their chief and no wife in his tent. They rose into the air and searched the sea. They grieved for the death of their chief and their mourning cries filled the air. Fulmars still mourn and cry like this today when they fly over the sea.

Soon they spied the fleeing boat carrying Sedna and her father. They stirred up a terrific storm, with heavy winds and high waves, and the two fugitives in the frail craft were doomed to drown.

In this great peril the father decided to save himself and throw Sedna to the avenging birds. So he threw her overboard. Sedna clung to the boat in terror, but the cruel father took a knife and chopped at her fingers.

The first joints fell into the sea and became whales. Still Sedna clung to the boat. The father chopped again and chopped off the stumps of her fingers. Thus from Sedna's suffering and terror the sea was filled with living creatures which have been a benefit to mankind ever since.

Sedna fell into the sea and the fulmars allowed the storm to subside, for they thought that she was drowned.

As soon as the sea was quiet again, Sedna climbed back into the boat. But she did not love her father after this, and one night soon after, when the old man was asleep, she called her dogs around her and told them to gnaw off his hands and feet.

The dogs set to, to avenge their mistress, and soon had his hands and feet off before he woke up. When he discovered what had happened to him he began to curse in a loud voice. He cursed himself; he cursed Sedna and the dogs. And the earth opened up and swallowed them all.

But before this happened, Sedna created the deer one

day in the hills, out of a small piece of fat. As soon as it was finished, as soon as she saw it, she was afraid of it. "Run away!" she said. But the deer would not run away; instead, it turned and ran *at* her, and Sedna knocked out its front teeth. Today the deer still have no front teeth.

Ever since the night the earth swallowed them, Sedna and her father and the dogs have lived in Adlivun. Sedna rules in Adlivun, in a big house with a big dog at the door. She sleeps on a bearskin; she has no deerskins in the house, for Sedna does not like the deer. The old man, the father, Anguta, lives there too; he sleeps most of the time, for he cannot walk around.

All the souls of the dead come to this house, and murderers never get out. The big dog moves aside just enough to let the souls come in. And they have to sleep side by side for one year with Anguta, who pinches them.

Every fall the Eskimo hold a great feast for Sedna. She is mistress of all fish and all sea creatures. And fishermen and hunters pray to her to send them fish and seals.

This is retold from the versions of the Sedna story in Franz Boas: *The Central Eskimo.*

RAVEN FINDS A CLAM

When the Haida Indians tell the story of Raven and how he created the world out of nothing, they call it the Old Man's story, and no one may laugh. As the story lengthens into Raven's ridiculous adventures of stealing the sun for mankind or stealing the halibut from a fisherman's hook and getting hooked himself, then the people may laugh.

But this is the first story: of the time when Raven was a god.

NOT LONG AGO, not long ago, there was nothing but open sea. And Raven was flying. Then one little small rocky island was in the sea, and Raven sat upon it.

"Become earth," he said, and it became the earth. Raven was a god in those days.

The earth spread and widened, and Raven divided it. He took a small piece and put it in the water on one side of him, and that is why this island is small (Queen Charlotte Island) ; but the earth on the other side is big.

51

One day he was walking along in the sand at the edge of the water, alone in the empty world, and heard a small sound.

He listened. He heard it again. He looked down at his feet. A clamshell was sticking up, half buried in the wet sand. It was just slowly opening. He heard a little voice.

Raven bent down and looked into it. He saw a little human face. "Come out," he whispered.

The little face looked at Raven and then pulled back into the clamshell.

Again Raven heard the little voice inside the shell. He leaned down. "Come out," he whispered. Two little heads appeared this time, then popped back in; and there was a babble of tiny voices.

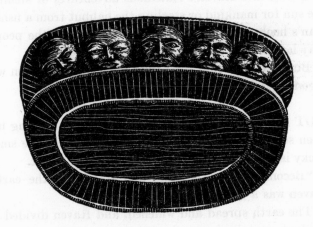

Haida Indian argyllite carving of mankind popping out of the clamshell. From a photograph in Marius Barbeau: *Haida Myths*, page 161.

Again and again he called to them and at last five small faces appeared. Some looked eager and curious; one had its eyes closed; some were smiling. They came out. They were people. Thus Raven drew mankind out of a clamshell and the world was peopled.

This story is based on the myth as found in John R. Swanton: *Haida Texts—Masset Dialect.* Jesup North Pacific Expedition, vol. 10, pt. 2 (1908); Marius Barbeau's "How the Raven Stole the Sun," *Transactions of the Royal Society of Canada,* 3rd Series, Section 2, vol. 38, 1944.

EARTH-WOMAN

THE CREATOR—named Chief, named Old-One—
made this world out of a woman. "She is the mother of
all people," he said. And she is here yet. The soil
is her flesh; the trees and grasses are her hair; her bones
are the rocks; and the wind is her breath. And all we
who live upon our mother, the earth, as she lies extended,
are the children of her flesh.

The earth was small at first, but Old-One rolled it out
and rolled it out until it was bigger, and he stretched it
out with its head to the west. Earth-Woman lies with

her head to the west. This is why all the great rivers flow west, and why west is the direction the souls take when they leave this world.

Old-One took up in his hands little pieces of earth and rolled them into small mud-balls, and from these he made the creatures. Some could fly and some could swim; some walked; some stood up. Each one had his own strength and his own weakness, his own gift of wisdom, and his own special foolishness.

Old-One made each little ball of earth into a different creature. He made each a different shape and he blew his breath upon the shapes and gave them life. Some of them were deer and some of them were Indians. These he called men, and these were the most helpless of all.

Some of the people were selfish and there was much trouble among them. So Old-One sent his son Jesus into the world to set things right. But the bad people killed Jesus; they crucified him and he went back to his father in the sky.

Then Old-One looked into this world again and saw that things were not much better. Jesus had told the people a lot of things; he had told them how to be good, but nobody had listened much.

So Old-One sent Coyote into the world to set things right. And Coyote traveled all over and did many, many things. He destroyed the monsters that killed the people, and showed the Indians how to spread out and live everywhere. He gave the tribes their names and taught them their different languages. He showed the people how to make houses, how to hunt and fish, and how to eat, how to make clothes and how to wear them. He put salmon in the rivers and showed the people how to fish with dipnets and spears. He saved mankind from being frozen by the Ice People, by killing them all with heat—all except one. If he had caught that one there would be no more cold or ice in the world.

"Your name is Cold," he shouted at her as she ran off. "You shall not kill people—just once in a while a lost, exhausted hunter."

But Coyote also made some very foolish mistakes and he never did get everything finished properly.

For instance, Coyote thought that water should not make a noise when it dropped. One day when he was walking along he heard water dropping. He sat down beside it and told it to stop. It went on—drop, drop, drop, drop.

"Keep quiet," he cried, but the water continued to drip, drip, drip, drip.

Coyote was enraged. He got up and kicked the place. And the water rushed out and came after him, increasing and roaring as it came. He ran, but the water followed him and covered him and swept him along, and Coyote was nearly drowned. Thus those few drops of water became the Columbia River. The Columbia River is a blessing to the people, but Coyote did not know he was going to make it! His mistake was not wanting water to make a noise, for thirsty hunters in the wilderness rejoice when they hear the sound of water.

When Old-One looked over the world again he said, "Well, Coyote has done all he is able to do. I shall have to finish this myself." So Old-One came into the world and traveled around as an old man, teaching the people.

One day he met Coyote walking along, who said, "Hello, who are you? I am Coyote."

56

"I am Chief of this world," said Old-One. "I sent you here to set things right."

"Oh, no, that wasn't *you!*" But Old-One said yes, he really was Old-One.

"If you are, pick up that lake and put it over there," said Coyote.

"If you are the wonderful Coyote, you do it," said Old-One. So Coyote did it.

"Now put it back," said Old-One.

But Coyote could not budge it. So Old-One put it back.

"Yes. You are Chief, you are Old-One," said Coyote.

"Well, your work is finished," Old-One told him. "You have done very well and now you may rest." So Coyote went off and no one knows where.

Then Old-One spoke to the people and said, "I too cannot stay in this world, but I will send messages to you, my people, by the souls that seek me out. These will deliver my messages. Listen to them.

"Some day when Earth-Woman is very old, I shall come again, and all the spirits of the dead will come with me. After that there will not be two worlds, but one. We shall all live together. And Earth-Woman will be seen by all eyes as the mother of her children."

The Okanagon Indians today say that Earth-Woman is now very old and her bones show through in many places. Therefore the time must be very near.

This is an Okanagon Indian story (Washington) retold from the three versions of their creation and Coyote stories collected by James Teit, in *Folktales of Salishan and Sahaptin Tribes,* edited by Franz Boas.

THE LIZARD-HAND

THE YOKUTS INDIANS of central California say that at first there was nothing but water, with an old stump sticking up out of it—the primeval stump. Some do say it was a mountain top—but this story says it was a stump.

There were several creators. Eagle was the chief one and Coyote was his assistant. Eagle was very wise. Coyote made a lot of mistakes and did some ridiculous things, but he brought about some very good things also.

Coyote was the one who advised Eagle to let Duck dive off the stump and bring up earth from the bottom of the sea to create the world. And Coyote was the one who later stole the sun to make light for the world.

When man was being shaped, Coyote and Lizard argued about the hands.

"The hand shall be like mine," said Coyote, "a good, solid fist."

58

"No. He needs fingers," said Lizard. "His hand shall be like mine."

Lizard held up his hand. "See!" he said. Lizard had five fingers.

So they argued back and forth. At last Coyote gave in. The man should have a lizard-hand. "All right," he said at last, "but then he will have to die after a while." And that is how man's hand was made and how death came into the world.

This story is based on material in A. L. Kroeber: *Handbook of the Indians of California,* 510*f.,* and the lizard-hand incident in Stith Thompson: *Tales of the North American Indians,* from Kroeber: *University of California Publications in American Archaeology and Ethnology* 4: 231 (1907).

NOBODY THERE

THERE WAS nobody there. Space was there and emptiness: *Kyuvish,* space; *Atahvish,* emptiness. These two called out to each other and became *Omai-Yaman,* which means "Nothing exists." Then came upheaval, the time when things were stirring and coming into shape, and a time when things were falling in various directions through space.

Then came the pale glimmering time, and the Milky Way, *Piwish,* was stretched across the emptiness. And after that came a time when all things were moving in the dimness, without the sun, without the moon; and deep down in the heart of the earth things were working together to become.

Then Kyuvish-Atahvish made a man, Tukomit, the sky; and a woman, Tamayowut, the earth.

Still there was no light, but these two knew there was somebody there.

Tukomit said, "Who are you?"

"I am stretched out; I am extended; I resound; I am earthquake; I revolve; I roll—who are you?"

"I am night; I am inverted over you; I am the arch of heaven; I cover; I seize; I devour."

"Brother!"

"And you are my sister, the Earth."

And thus by her brother, the Sky, did Tamayowut, the Earth, conceive and give birth to all the first things and creatures. Of these two were born the mountains and the rocks, stone and flint, and all the wooden objects the Luiseño used in their daily and religious life. Grasses, trees, and birds were born: black oak and cottonwood, the ash, brake ferns, rose and blackberry, tussock grass and sedge; the badger, the buzzard, the eagle, raven, bear, and fish, rattlesnake, spider, and the tarantula hawk. The ball of fire, the meteor, also came forth from the Earth, the meteor Takwish, who was so greatly feared. And from these two also was born Towish, the spirit of man which survives the body. Last of all Wiyot was born, and from Wiyot sprang all the generations of people.

All this happened in the north, in the dark. And as the people increased in numbers, the earth grew southward and the people followed it. They followed it south to Lake Elsinore and then to Temecula. Here, because of the darkness, one called Hainit Yunenkit made the sun, and the people raised it into the sky four times in a net before it would stay.

Here at Temecula, too, Wiyot died for the people and could not be saved.

"You are beautiful, my daughter," said Wiyot to

Frog. He had made her very carefully, with great big eyes. But when Frog saw the beautiful legs of mankind as they walked, she hated Wiyot for making her own so thin and crooked.

She spat in the spring where Wiyot drank and poisoned the water, and in ten months Wiyot died.

"I shall die in the spring when the grass is high," Wiyot told the people.

But before he left the earth he taught them everything they needed to know; he taught them how to make baskets and ollas; he gave them their laws and arts, and promised that from his ashes would come the most precious of all his gifts.

Out of his ashes grew the oak. It grew tall and lovely; the branches spread, and acorns hung on the tree, thick and ripening.

Then the people sent Crow to the big star to find Wiyot. But Crow could not find him. Eagle went next and came back unsuccessful. Then Hummingbird went and came back with the message:

"Eat the seeds of my tree. All birds and all animals, eat the seeds of my tree. All men, make flour from the seeds and make cakes from the flour."

So the people rejoiced and gathered the acorns and celebrated the harvest with the *bellota* festival, the acorn feast. Acorns were still a major part of the diet of the Luiseño Indians in the nineteenth century.

Wiyot himself returns to the people, for Wiyot is the moon.

"Wiyot rises! Wiyot comes!" the people cry. And they perform the dance which they hope will prevent his waning.

How deeply the Luiseño believe that they are children of the earth and sky is revealed in the boys' initiation ceremonies. A sand painting of the universe is made, showing the Milky Way, the sun and moon and the edge of the world, and other details, and the old men say to the boys, "See this. Everybody is going to see your goodness . . . The earth hears you; the sky and the mountains see you. If you believe this, you will grow old."

Rewritten and adapted from A. L. Kroeber: *Handbook of the Indians of California,* 677-678, 682, 684, and the two versions of the Wiyot story as given in C. G. DuBois: "Mythology of the Mission Indians," *Journal of American Folklore,* 17:183-188 (1904). See article "acorn" in the *Standard Dictionary of Folklore, Mythology, and Legend.*

A Luiseño Indian sand painting symbolizing the universe. The outer circle is the Milky Way. The second circle is "the sky, the night, the arch of heaven" which surrounds the earth. The third circle represents the root of existence, and the space between this and the sky symbolizes the imperishable soul of man. The fourth circle is the edge of the world itself. The four straight lines at right angles to each other, which divide the world into four quarters, are the hands and arms of the world. In the lower left quarter can be seen Rattlesnake, who is one of the punishers of people for their sins. To the left of Rattlesnake are three ceremonial baskets. The small circle in the center marks the little pit dug in the earth to symbolize death and burial and the abode of the dead; it is called "the navel of the universe." This explanation is taken from A. L. Kroeber: *Handbook of the Indians of California*, 662-664.

FROM-THE-BEGINNING-TALK

Zuni Emergence Myth

WHEN THE Zuni Indians tell the story of the emergence of mankind from under the earth in the beginning of the world, they call the tale "from-the-beginning-talk."

It was dark down there in the fourth world. The people were crowded together and it was so dark they could not see each other. They stepped on one another and if one wanted so much as to spit, he would spit on another. They were so crowded they could hardly breathe.

In the beginning the sun rose and the sun set and there was no one on the face of the earth. The Sun looked down upon the world and saw that it was clothed in green hills. There were bright clear springs and trees, but no people—no people to offer up prayer.

He pitied the people in the dark underworld and said, "Let them come up into the light." So he threw his rays into the mists that covered the earth and put it into the hearts of his two sons to find the people and show them the way.

One day Younger Brother said to Elder Brother, "This is a good world and nobody lives in it."

"True," said Elder Brother.

"Let us go southwest," said Younger Brother. "People are living down there in the fourth world without light. They cannot move or see. They should come up here where they can see our father the Sun."

"True," said Elder Brother.

So the two brothers traveled southwest until they came to the entrance to the lower world.

They entered and came to the first world. It was dim. They came to the second world. It was dark. They came to the third world. It was darker. They came to the fourth world. It was black. They could not see. The people were there, but they could not see them. The people knew someone had come; but they could not see.

"A stranger is here," one cried.

"Where are you from?" called another.

They put out their hands to touch the two sons of the Sun.

"We have come to bring you to the Sun," the two boys said.

"We have heard of our father the Sun," said the people.

"We long to see the Sun," they said.

"We have come for you," the two boys said again. "Will you come with us?"

"Yes," the people answered.

"Show us the way," they cried.

66

"Bring us to the Sun."

"Show us how."

Younger Brother went to the north and planted the seeds of the pine tree. He turned around once and the pine tree was grown; he turned once again and the branches were spread. He broke off a branch and took it to the people.

Then he went west and planted the seeds of the spruce. He looked aside and when he looked back, the spruce was grown. He looked away again, and when he looked back the branches were spread. He broke off a branch and took it down to the people.

Then Younger Brother went south and planted the seeds of the silver spruce. It grew miraculously, as the pine and spruce had done, and he broke off one branch and took it down to the people.

He went east then, and planted the seeds of the aspen tree. He turned around and the aspen was grown; he turned once more, and the branches had spread. He took one branch and carried it to the people.

"This is all," he said. "We are ready."

The two sons of the Sun made a long prayer stick from the pine tree of the north and the people climbed up into the third world. They heard a rumbling like thunder.

"Are you all out?"

"Yes," said the people. "Is this where we are to live?"

"Not yet," said the brothers. But they stayed there four days—or four years.

The sons of the Sun then made a long prayer stick from the spruce of the west and set it in the earth. The people climbed up it into the second world. It was twilight here and they were blinded.

"Are you all here?"

"Yes. Is this it? Is this the world?"

"Not yet," said the boys.

Then the two made a long prayer stick from the silver spruce of the south; and the people climbed up into the first world. It was red-dawnlight here and they covered their eyes because of the light.

"Is this the bright world where we are to live?"

"Not yet."

In this world the people could see each other and they did not like what they saw. They were a terrible-looking lot. They were dirty and stained. Green slime was growing on their heads. They had tails. Their hands and feet were webbed, and they had no mouths.

They remained in the first world four days. Then the two sons of the Sun made a long prayer stick from the aspen of the east and stuck it in the earth. There was a great roll of thunder, and the people climbed out into the daylight world.

When they came out into the sun, the tears streamed down their faces from the pain of light. They started to cover their eyes.

"Turn to the Sun," Younger Brother cried out. "Look full at your father the Sun, no matter how bright."

So the people turned their faces to the Sun's face. They cried aloud with the pain of the piercing light in their eyes and their tears poured on the ground.

The Sun's flowers sprang up from those tears: sunflowers and buttercups.

"This is the world," said the people.

"Yes. This is the world."

Zuni Indian petroglyph of a primitive Zuni before amputation of
tail. From a photograph in M. C.
Stevenson: *Zuni Indians,* page 42.

The people rested in that spot for four days, and then
traveled on. When they came to the ancient village of
Awico they stopped again, and the two brothers said, "It
is time to teach our people to eat."

So they planted corn in the fields and waited for it to
grow. When it had grown they harvested it and gave
the ears to the people. The people smelled it and were
pleased with it but they could not eat, for they had no
mouths. That night when the people were asleep, the

two brothers cut a mouth in every face. The knives made the lips red, because they had been sharpened on a red whetstone.

When the people woke up, they had mouths. They were hungry, and the two brothers gave them corn to eat and water to drink. They wanted to break up the corn so it would be easier to eat, so they rubbed it with their hands against the hearthstones and ground it into meal for porridge. Then it was hard to clean the porridge off their hands. It smeared and stuck to the webbed hands.

That night the two sons of the Sun sharpened their knives again. "Let's cut their fingers apart," they said. So while the people slept they cut apart the fingers and toes of the webbed hands and feet. The people had not been eating long enough to have good red blood, so they did not bleed. In the morning they were amazed at what had happened; but they got used to the change and found it more satisfactory.

After the people had eaten, they began to feel uncomfortable; they felt as if they would burst, for they had no way of getting rid of all they ate. "Poor things," said the brothers. And that night while the people slept they went into the houses and cut an outlet in everyone. And after that the people felt much better.

The next night the two brothers decided to cut the horns and tails off their people. So with the sharp stone knives they went into the houses again while the people slept to cut off the horns and the tails. A few woke up and said they did not want their tails cut off—and the descendants of these are the monkeys.

In the morning when the rest of the people woke up,

they looked just as people look today. They were amazed at themselves, but they were pleased with the change and they were certainly glad they were finished.

Retold from the versions of this myth as presented by Ruth Benedict: *Zuni Mythology,* vol. 1, and Ruth Bunzel: *Zuni Origin Myths,* 584*ff.*

FIT TO LIVE

IN THE BEGINNING there was nothing at all but darkness, water, and cyclones. There was no earth, no people, no animals, no fish in the water.

Only the spirits were here, the great spirits and powers who existed before time began.

They made the earth first, and then the sky. But that did not seem to be enough.

Creator was the chief of them all. He was the first one to make an animal. He knew how to do it.

So he made an animal out of clay. He put four legs on it, and then he made a tail.

"Walk on the four feet," he said.

The animal walked.

"That's pretty good," said the Creator. "You are all right. Now run along."

Then he made all the rest of the animals. He made some with horns and some without horns: he made bears, deer, horses, sheep, cows, wildcats, birds, everything.

As soon as they were made they asked Creator what they should eat. So he told them.

He told each animal what kind of food it should eat, and where to live. Some went into the mountains, some to the desert, some to the plains, some to the forests. Some went into the lakes and rivers; some dug little holes in the ground. They spread out all over the earth in their own special places.

All this time Dog was going around with Creator. Everywhere he went, Dog went, and watched all that he did. When Creator finished one job and moved on to another, the dog went too.

"Are you going to stay around here all the time?" said the dog. "Or will you have to go away?"

"Well, perhaps someday I shall have to live far away," said Creator.

"Then, Grandfather, will you make me a companion?"

So Creator lay down on the ground.

"Draw a line around me with your paw," he said.

So Dog scratched an outline in the earth all around the great Creator. Creator got up and looked at it.

"Go a little ways off and don't look," he said.

The dog went off a little way. In a few minutes he looked.

"Oh, someone is lying where you were lying, Grandfather."

"Go along and don't look," said Creator.

The dog went a little farther. In a few minutes he looked.

"Someone is sitting there, Grandfather," he said.

"Turn around and walk farther off," said Creator.

The dog obeyed.

At last Creator called the dog. "Now you can look," he said.

"Oh, Grandfather, he moves," cried the dog in delight.

So they stood by the man and looked him over.

"Pretty good," said Creator.

"He's wonderful," said the dog.

Creator went behind the man and lifted him to his feet.

"Put out your foot," he said. "Walk. Do this."

So the man walked.

"Now run," Creator said.

He took hold of the man and showed him how to run. The man ran.

"Talk," said Creator. But the man said nothing. Four times Creator told the man to talk. "Say words," he said. Finally the man said words. He spoke.

"Now shout," said Creator. He gave a big yell himself and showed the man how.

The man shouted.

"What else?" he said.

Creator thought a minute.

"Laugh," he said. "Laugh, laugh, laugh, laugh."

Then the man laughed.

The dog was very happy when the man laughed. He jumped up on him and ran off a little, and ran back and jumped up on him. He kept jumping up on him the way dogs do today when they are full of love and delight.

The man laughed and laughed.

"NOW YOU ARE FIT TO LIVE," said Creator.

So the man went off with his dog.

This is part of the long creation myth of the Jicarilla Apache Indians of New Mexico, based on the material presented by Morris Edward Opler: *Myths and Tales of the Jicarilla Apache Indians.*

OLD MAN

LONG AGO there was nothing but water. There was no earth and there were no living creatures except Old Man, and four ducks. Old Man was sometimes called Old-Man-Coyote.

Old Man came along and spoke to the ducks.

"Is there any earth down there?"

"Yes," they said.

"Go bring some." He spoke first to the red-headed mallard. "Dive down and bring up some earth and we'll make a world," he said.

The mallard dived and stayed down so long that they thought he was drowned. At last he came back, but he brought no earth.

"You try," said Old Man to the pinto duck. The pinto dived and stayed a long time. At last he came back. "I couldn't get any," he said.

Old Man next sent down the blue-feathered duck, but he too came back without any.

Then the helldiver said, "Old Man, send me." So Old Man said, "All right."

Helldiver, the fast little dabchick, flashed into the great primeval water out of sight. He was gone a long time. Old Man and the three ducks waited and waited. Was Helldiver dead, they wondered? At last he came.

"Any luck?" said Old Man.

"Brother, I have a little," said Helldiver.

"For every undertaking, the fourth try succeeds," said Old Man. "Where is it?"

"Here," said Helldiver. There was a little mud in the ends of his long-lobed toes.

Old Man took the little bit of mud in his hand.

"Now I shall make the earth for you," he said, "and you shall live in the ponds and streams."

Then with the mud in his hand Old Man started from the east and began to mark out the edges of the world. He started in the east and traveled westward.

"Let's have it large enough," he said, and he spread the mud out and made this big world. He made rivers and springs and creeks, mountains and hills and trees.

"Here is the earth," he said, "now there are others who wish to live."

A howling was heard. "Already one is howling," said Old Man. And a coyote came running out of the west.

"There is greatness and power in this one," said Old Man. "For he came by himself."

Then Old Man made the buffalo out of mud and all the other animals. The animals said, "I want to be like this," or "——— like this"; and Old Man made each one the way it wished to be.

Then he made the people. There was a hole opening into a hollow tree. He pounded on it with a stick. "Come out," he cried. And the people came out.

"Look around," said Old Man. "Look at your world." Then he saw that the people had no eyes and could not see the wonderful new world. With his fingers Old Man made holes for the eyes of the first one and told him to do the same for the next. So each man that came out of the tree turned around and made eyes for the next. These were the Crow Indians.

Then Old Man walked over the plains, and Cirape, the little coyote, went with him. Old Man named him Cirape, which means Younger Brother. They walked along. "There shall be stones all over the earth," said Old Man. And there are.

They saw someone standing up far away. "There is one of the stars from above," said Old Man. But when they came to the place, the star had changed into a white-flowered plant.

"This is the tobacco plant," said Old Man. "The stars above have taken this form for the sake of man. Let man care for it and use it. It will mean life and comfort to him."

Then Old Man showed the people their food and how to make tepees. He showed them how to make arrows, with bird feathers for feathering and sharp stones for the tips. He showed them how to make a keen edge on a stone and use it for a knife and how to make fire with the fire-drill.

"Take two sticks," he said, "and put a little sand on one of them with some *very dry* buffalo manure. Then take the other stick and twist it between your hands until fire comes."

Thus Old Man taught the people all their ways for living a good life. He gave the people dogs to carry their things; he gave them sleep and dreams and everything he told them to do, they did. Most of the people were strong-hearted. But some of them, they say, are not strong of heart and want to take revenge if they are mistreated.

This story is rewritten and adapted from the three versions of the Crow creation tale in Robert H. Lowie: *Myths and Traditions of the Crow Indians* and from material in S. C. Simms: *Traditions of the Crows.*

IT WAS TURNING

IN THE BEGINNING when Earthmaker became, when Earthmaker, the creator, slowly came to consciousness, he was sitting there, and nothing was there. And he took a little piece of that on which he was sitting and made this world. He threw it down and it went spinning and turning through space.

Then he looked down at it. Nothing was growing on it and he saw that it was turning.

So Earthmaker thought he would make hair for the world. He made grass and threw it down. It covered the earth. But the earth was still turning.

"A tree," he thought. So he made a tree and sent it down. Trees took hold and grew all over the earth, but when Earthmaker looked at the earth he had made, it was still turning.

Then he made the four brothers of the directions and sent one to the east, one to the north, one to the west, and one to the south to hold the world still. But when he looked again, it was still turning.

Then he scattered the rocks over the earth. They pierced through the deep body of the world and when Earthmaker looked down, only their heads were sticking out. These were the mountains. The weight of them steadied the earth. There were no clouds and a great light lay over everything. It looked as quiet as a summer day.

Earthmaker thought there should be walkers-in-the-light, so he made the birds to fly through the air. There should be four-legged walkers on the land, he thought, so he made the animals and established the places for each kind to live. He made the fish to swim in the sea. He created as many insects as the world should have and scattered them everywhere.

Then at the end of his thinking, he thought of putting mankind upon the earth. So he created human beings, last of all, least of all, weakest of all.

Earthmaker made man out of a little piece of earth and shaped it like himself. Then he spoke to the man, but the man did not answer. He did not hear. So Earthmaker put his finger into his own right ear, and then into the ear of the man. Then he spoke to the man again. The man could hear, but he did not answer. He could not see. So Earthmaker touched his own eyes, then the eyes of the man, and the man could see.

Earthmaker spoke to him again, but still the man did not speak. So he put his finger on his own lips and then touched the lips of the man. The man could speak, but he did not know what to say. Earthmaker then perceived that the man had neither mind nor heart. So he breathed his own breath into the mouth of the man, and the man breathed and his heart was full.

Earthmaker spoke to the man again and the man answered his creator; very nicely and quietly he answered.

Earthmaker then sent the man into the world. When he came to the very center, there he split and was dispersed. And thus all the different peoples and all the languages came into existence.

This is the Winnebago story of creation based on the three versions of the myth in Paul Radin: *Origin Myth of the Medicine Rite.*

Seneca Indian Creation Stories

Here are two creation stories told by the Seneca Indians, one of the famous tribes of the Iroquois Nation. *On Turtle's Back* is the old, old story. It is the creation myth of all the Iroquois tribes. Each version varies slightly, however, in the names and details. The modern folktale about the creation of man has no relationship to the ancient Iroquois mythology. It is a *why story*, explaining the different colors of mankind, and the creator is not an old Seneca deity but is called God, like the creator in the Christian story.

On Turtle's Back

IN THE BEGINNING all was water and on the surface of the water swam ducks and loons, helldivers, and waterfowl of many kinds, and Turtle. Toad was there too. There was no land, no earth, for the foot of man.

All the first people lived in the sky and for food gathered the fruit of a wonderful tree which grew beside the chief's lodge.

One day the chief's daughter sickened; many remedies were collected and given her, but no cure was found. The girl weakened and was like to die. Then it was revealed to a man in a dream that the girl should be laid beside the tree and the tree should be dug up.

This was done. While the digging was going on, a young man came along who said, "This is wrong! Why destroy the food-tree just for her!" And he gave the girl a resentful kick with his foot which flung her into the hole, and she began to fall.

She fell, turning, a long way through space—and then the birds on the water saw her.

"We'll catch her! We'll catch her!" they cried. And they rose in the air and spread their wings and pressed close together, and the young girl fell on this bed of living feathered birds. They upheld her safely so that she did not drown.

At last they tired and cried, "Who will take care of her now?"

"I'll take her," Turtle said, and so for a period the young girl slept, unknowing and safe, on the back of Turtle. After a while Turtle too got tired.

"Who'll take her?" he asked. And then the creatures realized they must find some permanent resting-place for the girl.

"There ought to be an earth," they said. But how to make it?

"Is there earth in the bottom of the sea?" they wondered.

Toad said she would go and find out. Turtle said if they made the earth, he would support it on his back, so that there would be room for it to spread and accommodate newcomers.

So Toad dived down; bravely she dived into the dark primeval water, and finally returned with a little soil from the bottom of the sea. The creatures spread this over Turtle's back, and at once it began to spread out and Turtle himself began to grow.

The birds laid the young girl gently on the earth and when she woke up and was well, she made herself a little house and was very comfortable. Bushes began to grow upon the earth, and the girl walked here and there and all around the edge of it, to see and admire what the creatures had done. And after a while she gave birth to a baby girl.

This child grew up in the house with her mother, helping to dig potatoes and do the chores of woman, and in time she too gave birth to twins—two boys. One was red, named Othagwenda (Flint), and the other was fair, named Juskaha (Sapling).

The grandmother loved Juskaha but did not like the Flint boy very much, so she took him out of the house and left him in a hollow tree. Juskaha, the fair twin, grew fast and learned to make bows and arrows and to hunt. Every day he would go out and hunt and every night he came home with something to eat. After a while he began to come home very late, and without the bows and arrows. He would sit down and make new ones in the morning before he went out. After this had happened several times the grandmother said one day, "Where is your bow? Where are your arrows?"

"I gave them to the boy in the tree."

"What tree?" said the grandmother.

"There is a boy who lives in a hollow tree near here," said Juskaha, "and he needs them."

One night when Juskaha came in he brought the twin brother with him. And from that time on the boys lived and played and hunted together. But Othagwenda, who had been cast out, had grown mischievous and ill-willed.

The boys grew and thrived and every day went out into the world together to hunt. One day they said, "This earth-island is a small place," and decided to enlarge it. They would make lakes and forests and a lot of other things, they said. So they set out.

Othagwenda went west and Juskaha turned east. That night in their shelter they agreed to go look at each other's work the next day.

Morning came. They went and looked at Othagwenda's creations. He had made a region full of jagged rocks and ledges, and a big mosquito.

"Run," said Juskaha to the mosquito. He wanted to see what it was like.

So the mosquito ran, and to show off, stuck his bill through a young tree and felled it.

"This is not good," said Juskaha. "You might kill the people we are going to make."

Juskaha grabbed him by the neck and rubbed him down to the size mosquitoes are now. Then he blew him away and the mosquito flew off. But he has been mad ever since and bites everyone he can.

The next day they went to look at Juskaha's handiwork, and Othagwenda did not like it. Juskaha had made some of the animals very fat and slow-moving. He had made the sugar-maple tree with the sirup dripping off the ends of the branches. Othagwenda soon changed all this.

"Everything will be too easy for the people," he said.

He took hold of the animals and shook the fat off them and they became small and timid and elusive, as the deer and hare and the partridge are today. And he fixed the sugar maple so that it dripped thin sweet water wherever it was tapped, and man would have to make his own sirup.

The brothers were so displeased with each other's creations that they quarreled, and then they fought, and Othagwenda was killed.

Modern Seneca Folktale of Creation

GOD CREATED the sun and moon first, and then one day, as he walked lonely in the world, he said, "I'll make someone to keep me company."

He walked along, thinking about how he would do this, and came to a hemlock which had been overturned by the wind. The roots had raised a great mound of earth as they broke out of the ground. The roots were many and slender and haired with many tiny feeders.

"I shall make man from this earth," said God. So he shaped a man and breathed upon him and gave him life, then hid behind the tree to watch and see what he was like. God was not pleased with the man, for he had a pale, sickly color from the light-colored soil in which the hemlock grew, and he was covered with hair from the many-fibered roots which had broken off in the earth. So he thought he would try again. He walked along until he came to a walnut tree uprooted, and the broken earth around its upturned roots was black. So he made man from this. He shaped the man and breathed upon him and gave him life. But when the man stood up and walked away, God said, "Too dark. I'll try once more."

God walked along and walked along and finally came upon a sugar maple tree lying uprooted. The earth around the upturned roots was a good rich color. So God took this wonderful earth in his hand and shaped a man. The body was smooth and firm and deep-tinted. And when God saw him move he said, "Ha! He looks like me!" This was the first Seneca Indian.

Both of the above tales are retold from the Seneca material collected by Jeremiah Curtin and J. B. N. Hewitt: *Seneca Fiction, Legends, and Myths.*

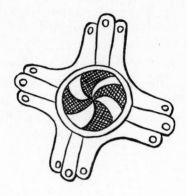

WHO?

This story of the beginning of the world is a story told by the Yuchi Indians of eastern Tennessee to the Creeks, their Georgia, South Carolina, and Florida neighbors, with whom they united for the protection of numbers after the coming of the white man.

IN THE BEGINNING there was only water. And Someone said, "Who will make the land?"

"I will make the land," said Crawfish. And he dived down to the bottom of that great sea and stirred up the mud with his eight legs and his tail. And he took the mud in his fingers and made a little pile.

The owners of the mud down there said, "Who is stirring up the mud?" And they watched to see. But Crawfish kept stirring up the mud with his tail so that they could not see.

88

Every day Crawfish dived into the deep water and got a little more mud and put it on the pile. Day by day he piled it up. At last one day as he piled the mud on top of the pile, his hands came out of the water into the air! At last the land appeared above the water.

It was very soft, for it was mud.

Someone said, "Who will stretch out the land? Who will make it hard? Who will make it dry?"

Buzzard stretched out the earth and dried it. He spread his long wings and stretched it. He sailed over the earth; he spread it wide and dried it. Then, tiring, he had to flap his wings and this made the mountains and valleys.

Someone said, "Who will make the light?"

Star said, "I will make light." But it was not enough.

It was said, "Who will make more light?"

"I will make light," said Moon. But it was still night.

Someone said, "More light."

Sun said, "I will make light. I am the mother."

So Sun moved over into the east, and all at once a great beautiful light spread over the world. And then as Sun moved from east to west, a drop of her blood fell and sank into the earth. From this blood and this earth came forth the first people, the Yuchi Indians. They called themselves *Tsohaya*, People of the Sun, and every man who took this name had a picture of the sun on his door.

This tale is based on the myth in the W. O. Toggle Collection in the Bureau of American Ethnology, presented by John R. Swanton: *Myths and Tales of the Southeastern Indians.*

IV
Central American Indian

IN THE DAY OF OBSCURITY

This is the ancient Mixtec Indian legend of creation. It begins with the beautiful words:

"IN THE YEAR and in the day of obscurity and darkness, when there were as yet no year and no day, the world was chaos sunk in darkness." The whole earth was covered with water. Green slime floated on the surface of the water and the scums moved gently in the dark.

One day came the god, in human form, and his beautiful goddess. This heavenly pair, out of their vast, unfathomed knowledge, raised a steep cliff over the abyss of water and on top of it built a fine dwelling for themselves. On the topmost point of the smooth cliff they laid a copper ax, edge up, and on this sharp edge rested the sky.

For hundreds of years the gods lived in happiness. Two little sons were born to them, and the ancient Mixtec calendar shows the days of their birth. Wind 9 Snake was the day the first was born; Wind 9 Cave was the birthday of the other.

These two possessed great power: they could become invisible, or turn themselves into snakes or eagles. They lived and played in a little garden high on the dark cliff, and could see the primeval water far below.

As they grew older they learned to plow the garden. They planted seeds, and flowers, trees, and herbs grew up around them. They burned tobacco for the gods and made this prayer:

> Let the light come.
> Let the water be held
> In little hollow places.
> Let the earth be freed
> Of the vast covering water,
> For this small dry place is all there is.

Time went by, but at last the prayer was answered. The creator formed the sky above, freed the earth of water and made it as it is, and allowed mankind to roam upon it.

The great cliff and the house of the gods is said to be in what is now Oaxaca, Mexico, near Apoala (which means "accumulation of water"). This was the Mixtec Yuta-Tmoho, the river of generation. And here the first Mixtecs, the first people, were born of the trees which grew by the steep cañada.

This story is based on Eduard Siler's presentation of the myth from Fray Gregorio Garcia's *Origen de los Indios,* chapter 4, in *Mexican Antiquities,* Bureau of American Ethnology, Bulletin 28, 1904.

The Aztec Indians of old Mexico conceived of their universe as both vertical and horizontal, overlayed with an intricate pattern of religious concepts.

They pictured the vertical universe as a series of upper and lower worlds, layer on layer, with the earth between them. There were nine (sometimes thirteen) upper worlds, of which the top four were occupied by the gods, with one for the sun, one for the moon, and one for the planets, stars, etc.

The vertical universe, as shown here, is a great simplification of the concept, showing only: at top, two gods playing ball with a death's head between them, and symbolizing the motion of the planets in the sky; below this, the sun disk; below the sun, a flint knife representing, in conventionalized pattern, the moon. At the bottom is shown the toad-faced mask of the monstrous Lord of the Earth, Tlaltecuhtli, waiting with open mouth to receive the setting sun, for the Aztecs believed that the sun disappeared into the earth at night and emerged from the earth at dawn.

Redrawn from a photograph of a gold pendant in the collection of the Museo Regional de Oaxaca, Mexico.

95

The Aztecs depicted their horizontal universe as laid out in five directions: east, south, west, north, and center. Here are the five regions as shown in *Codex Fejérvary-Mayer: An Old Mexican Picture Manuscript in the Liverpool Free Public Museum.*

The middle region is presided over by the Fire God, named Huehueteotl, which means the Old, Old God.

As is usual in ancient Aztec manuscripts, the top section represents the east. Here stands the Tree of the East, with flowers growing from the tips of the branches and the quetzal bird perched in the top. The east was the region of fertility and abundance. Tonatiuh, the Sun God, stands below the tree to the left. Quetzalcoatl, God of Knowledge and Civilization, in his cone-shaped hat, stands under it to the right, and the morning star, with which he is associated, is also shown.

In the right-hand section stands the Tree of the South, bearing flowers and fruits pointing downward from the trunk. A parrot sits in the top. The south was a region of spring and rain and vegetation and flowers, over which Tlaloc, the Rain God, and Mixcoatl, the Cloud God, presided. Tlaloc, with a big ring around his eye, with his teeth hanging down, and the scroll emerging from his mouth, is always easily recognizable. He *should* be standing to the left of the Tree of the South, but the old Aztec artist who drew this map mistakenly put him in the north and doubled the error by showing the Death God (who belongs in the north) standing to the left of the Tree of the South (where Tlaloc should be). But the south was also regarded as an evil region, hence the Lord of Death often turned up in the south, as here.

In the bottom section is the Tree of the West, its trunk covered with sprouts and in the top, a humming-bird. To the right stands the ancient earth goddess, Tlacolteotl, recognizable by the fillet around her head and the spindle in her hair.

In the left-hand section is the Tree of the North, its trunk and branches set with thorns and an eagle in the top. The north was a region of awfulness and cold, of thorny plants and

death, killing droughts and wars. The Lord of Death, named Mictlantecutli, *should* be shown here, to the left of the tree. He is unmistakable with his death's-head eye and teeth. But (as just explained) he appears in the south in this picture.

The figures between the four directional regions are the symbols of the four quarters of the sacred almanac of the Aztecs and the signs for the twenty day-names of the Aztec month.

This explanation follows Eduard Seler's commentary in *Codex Vaticanus B.*

THE HEARTLESS PEOPLE

IN THE BEGINNING there was nothing but sky and
the great sea. There were no animals or birds or fishes,
no trees, no stones or grasses, no forests, no people. There
was no sound, no motion.

There was only the creator, Tepeu, and Gucumatz, the
maker.

They talked together in the night and planned to create
the earth, to let dawn come in the sky, and to form mankind.

"Let the waters recede," they said. The waters with-
drew into the oceans.

"EARTH," they said. And there was the earth.

"Let there be light," they said. "Let the sun rise into
the sky and shine upon the earth."

Mountains rose up out of the water and the rivers ran
between them. Then they created trees and thickets and
all that lives and scurries in the world.

98

Next they made the animals, the birds, the pumas, the jaguars, the snakes and vipers, and all the little things that flit through bushes.

They made the deer. "Live in the forests and beside the rivers," they said.

They made the birds. "Live in the trees and vines," they told them. "Make nests; have young."

"Shall there be only silence?" said the gods. "No. Speak, cry, warble, sing, call—each with his own voice." And so it is.

But the creatures could not speak the names of the gods. And they wished, therefore, to make other creatures who would speak their names. So they began again.

"Let us make man," they said, "one who will remember his creator while he walks on the earth."

First they made a man of mud and clay. But he was no good. He was soft; he fell down. The waters washed him away.

Then they made a man of wood. Carefully they carved and shaped the wood. "These shall talk and speak," they said.

The new men rose up and walked and talked on the earth. They had sons and daughters. But they had no souls. They had no hearts and no love. They did not remember the creators. They spoke but their faces did not change. They did not smile. They never gave thanks for the earth under their feet, or for the rains, or for the wonder of light.

They existed in great numbers but they remembered nothing. They looked down as they walked along. They never looked up. They did not remember. They loved nothing.

So the whole world turned against them because they were heartless. The great eagle came and gouged out their eyes. The jaguars ate their flesh. The tapirs came and broke their bones. And while this was going on the black rains rained down.

The sticks and stones struck their faces. The earthen jars, the griddles, the plates and pots and bowls and cups, and the *metates* (grinding stones) all rose up and banged around and attacked them.

The dogs said, "You gave us nothing to eat. You kicked us out while YOU were eating. You had sticks in your hands to strike us. Now we bite back." And the dogs bit them.

The metates said, "Every day you ground our faces *huqui, huqui* (squeak, squeak). Now we grind you." And the metates began to grind the people to powder.

The griddles and pots said, "You burned us. You blackened our faces in the fire. Now we burn you." And

100

the griddles and pots began to burn and boil the people.

The plates and jars and bowls and cups all hurled themselves through the air at the people. And the three hearthstones on every hearth also hurled themselves through the air at their heads.

The people ran. They ran everywhere trying to get away. They climbed up on the roofs of the houses and the roofs fell in with them. They tried to climb into the trees, but the trees pulled their branches up. They tried to hide in caves, and the rocks clapped shut against them.

Thus the heartless men were destroyed. Only a few escaped and clung shivering and chattering to the trees. These today are the little monkeys. And this is why the monkeys look like men.

The next people were a better lot.

This story and the next are retold from the *Popol Vu,* the creation myth of the ancient Maya-Quiché Indians of Guatemala.

A BETTER LOT

"OF WHAT shall we make the flesh of man?"

Tepeu, the creator, and Gucamatz, the maker, sat talking in the night. They longed to finish the work; they longed for man to walk on the face of the earth and speak their names.

"Of what shall we make the flesh of man?" they said. And they sat, thinking and discussing in the night, before the sun and the moon and the stars were over their heads.

Four animals came and told them to go to Paxil. The mountain lion (*yac*), the coyote (*utiú*), the little parrot (*quel*), and the crow (*hoh*) came to Tepeu, the creator, and Gucumatz, the maker, and said that yellow ears and white ears were growing there in abundance.

So the gods went to Paxil. The animals showed them the road. And in that place Xmucané, Old Woman Grandmother, who was there, ground the ears of white and yellow corn and made nine broths.

From this nourishment the three of them created the flesh and the muscles and the strength of man. Of yellow and white corn-meal they made the arms and legs. Thus the first four men were created, the first ancestors of the human race.

The names of the first four men were Balam-Quitzé, Balam-Acab, Mahucutah, and Iqui-Balam. They were wonderful men. They spoke and walked; they could see

102

far; they could see the whole world at once, and far into the sky. Their wisdom was great; they understood everything.

Tepeu, the creator, and Gucumatz, the maker, said to them, "How are you? Do you see the world? Can you hear and speak?"

"We give thanks," said the men, "that we have been created. We thank our creators for sight and hearing; we walk and speak; we feel. We see heaven and earth and the four corners of the sky, and we know all that is far and near. We give thanks, O Tepeu, O Creator, O Gucumatz, O Maker, O Xmucané, O Grandmother."

Thus the new people gave thanks to the gods and spoke their names. But the gods were troubled.

"Perhaps they know too much," they said. "Perhaps they see too far. We meant to make simple people who would populate the earth."

So Tepeu, the creator, and Gucumatz, the maker, and Xpiyacoc, the grandfather, who was also there, and Xmucané, the grandmother, said, "Let them see only what is near; let them see only a small part of the earth at once." And they changed the nature of the people and made them less.

The creators blew mist into their eyes and dimmed their sight until they could see only what was near at hand. And the wonderful wisdom and knowledge of the men was made small.

Then the gods made wives for the men. Very carefully they made four women and laid them to sleep beside the men. And when they wakened, the hearts of the men were filled with joy, for the women were beautiful. These were the mothers of all of us.

GOD WINS

Here is a modern Maya Indian creation story.

IN A GREEN PASTURE God was born of the Virgin Mother, and the ox came and looked and breathed upon him to give him life.

"Who is the father of our sister's child?" said the Ancient Men, the brothers of the Virgin Mother. "Whose son is this?"

Three days after God was born, he spoke. When the Ancient Men heard that, they said, "Come along," and they took him with them to put him to work. They gave young God an ax and told him to clear away the trees. God gave two chops with the ax and the whole field was cleared.

This was more than the brothers could do in a week, and they were afraid. They did not like this; they struck him with whips and they gave him no food when the day's work was done. They took him home that night to his mother and said, "Tomorrow we will take our brother to work again."

"No," said the Virgin Mother, "he is too small."

"But I want to go," said God. "I want to see them burn the field." It was the custom of the Maya Indians first to clear a field of trees and then to burn it off before planting.

So the next day God went along with the brothers. But when they came to burn the field, they tied God with a rope to a tree in the middle of it before they set fire to the brush, and then they stood in a circle around the fire, waiting. "His stomach will boil and burst," they said. They could not see him for the flames and the smoke.

When God saw the fire leaping toward him, he called

to the little rodents in the earth, and the little rodents came out of their holes and gnawed the ropes and God escaped with them deep into their burrows, safe from the burning field.

"He is burned; we are rid of him," said the Ancient Men when the smoke lifted and they saw that he was gone.

But that night on their way home they saw God playing in front of his mother's hut. "We sent him home ahead," the Ancient Men told the Virgin Mother. "We were afraid he would get burned."

That night in their houses, the Ancient Men were unhappy and afraid.

"We have not conquered our sister's son," they said. "We must dance."

So the brothers brought out the drum and the chirimía (oboe). They put on their masks and costumes and then they danced.

"I am going to watch my brothers dance," said the Mother of God.

"I will go with you," said God.

"No, they will trample you."

"I can go in the cotton basket and watch."

So God went along in his mother's cotton basket and watched the dance of the Ancient Men.

When the dance was over, the brothers sat down to a feast.

"I want to see what they are eating," said God. So he looked. And when the men saw God watching, they threw the bones from their meat in his face.

God picked all the bones up very carefully and put them in his hat. He took them home and planted them in the earth nearby, and then built a corral around the place. In three days he went to look. Inside the corral he saw cattle and horses, pigs, deer, sheep, goats, armadillos, chickens, ducks, turkeys and geese, rabbits, squirrels, foxes, coyotes, badgers, raccoons, snakes, mice, birds, owls and songbirds and woodpeckers and sparrows, lizards, toads, frogs, iguanas, scorpions, turtles, cockroaches, dogs and cats, butterflies, ants, fleas and lice, and lions. Thus God planted all the animals there are in the world.

The Ancient Men came along and saw the corral and all the animals, so they opened it and most of the animals ran out. The horses, the sheep, the cattle, the pigs and chickens, the dog and the goat stayed behind in the corral. The wild animals ran into the forests and the birds flew away.

God said to his mother, "Now I am going to make a fiesta, a dance, like that of the Ancient Men."

But she laughed at him. "Not likely!" she said. "It takes money and food."

But God did it. "It will begin at midnight," he said.

Midnight came. The Ancient Men heard the sky-rockets and ran to see the dance of God. It was better than theirs and they felt ashamed.

They said to young God, "We have been mean to you. Please forgive us and show us where you got those wonderful costumes." They wanted to throw away their old dance costumes and get new ones like God's.

"All right," said God, "but the place is far away. The traveling is hard. There is cramp on the road and bitter cold and need for prayer. But come, I will show you."

They went. The mountains were steep; the rocks were sharp; it was cold. Their legs cramped from the difficult climbing, and the Ancient Men stopped oftener and oftener to pray that they might endure it.

When they came to a big tree by the path, God said, "Climb it, my brothers," so the brothers went up.

The tree started to grow. The brothers went on climbing and the tree went on growing. And God willed that they should stay there and went home and left them.

"Where are the brothers?" said his mother.

"Far away," said God.

"Where's that?"

"I will show you," said God. When they came to the tree, it was full of monkeys.

"Is this you?" said the Virgin Mother. But they could not answer now. They leaped from branch to branch and looked at God and his mother. One threw down something and hit the Mother of God in the eye.

"Stay there!" she said. "It serves you right." So God

and his mother went home. And this is why the monkeys are called "brothers of God."

But this was not the end of God's troubles. The foreign kings came running after him, and so God ran away.

On the way he saw a man planting. "What are you doing?" asked God.

"I am planting beans."

"In three days they will be ready," said God. "I am being hunted," said God. "Do not tell them I was here today." And he hurried off.

When the kings came to that place they saw a man gathering his beans.

"Have you seen God?" they said.

"Yes," said the man. "He passed by the day I was planting beans." The kings figured that was sixty days ago. But they followed God's trail.

After a while the kings caught him and killed him. Then they nailed him to the cross and went away.

God put a ladder on the cross and climbed up it into heaven. As soon as God arrived in heaven, a great light shone all over the world. There was the sun for the first time.

The cock crowed right away. The beasts in the forest howled; the cattle lowed. The wicked kings were burnt up by the sun's heat. And the world God had made was lighted with a great clear light.

This story was told to Dr. Morris Siegel in 1941 in San Miguel Acatán Department of Huehuetenango in the Western Highlands of Guatemala. See his "The Creation Myth and Acculturation in Acatán, Guatemala," in *Journal of American Folklore* 56:120-126.

SUN-PAPA

THE SUMU INDIANS of Honduras and Nicaragua say that the world was created by two brothers. And the elder was named Papañ (pronounced pa-pang'). This is the Sumu word for papa or father.

First the two brothers made the hills and the forests; together they dug the rivers and made the blue lagoons; and then they shaped the savannas. The savannas are wide treeless plains or grasslands, covered with low shrubs and bush. And then they went paddling on the river in a small canoe, looking around to see what they should make next.

While they were shooting one of the wild white rapids the canoe capsized and threw the two brothers out into the swirling water. And they both struck out for shore, swimming well and fast.

When they got ashore, dripping wet, they were cold, so they made a fire. Then they felt hungry and looked around for something to eat. Not far away they found maize growing plentifully, so they plucked the ears and roasted them at the fire, and ate and were fed and satisfied.

Papañ threw his empty corncobs on the ground, and wherever they touched the ground they suddenly were changed into animals. Papañ kept eating the maize and throwing the cobs on the ground, and the animals kept rising from the empty cobs and running off into the bush.

Then Papañ threw some into the river and these became fish and swam away. And some which he threw never landed anywhere, but flew off in the air. These were the birds.

Papañ was astonished at these wonderful creations and stared after them. He kept making more and more until the earth was filled with creatures of the land and air and sea. And their beauty was such that Papañ could not tear his eyes away.

While he was gazing upward at a bird as it winged along, he forgot the fire and stepped backward into it and was caught in the flames. And as he burned he rose higher and higher in the air himself and became the sun. The younger brother watched him rise and finally could see only one fiery spot in the sky.

He stood there looking up, waiting for Papañ to come back, and he too forgot the fire and stepped into it and was caught in the flames. But this younger brother did not want to fly into the sky; he wanted to stay on the earth. And so he kicked and struggled and fought to keep from rising, and he made such a commotion that the sparks whirled around him and spiraled into the sky and scattered and became the stars.

But the younger brother struggled in vain. He did rise into the sky anyway, though not so far as his brother. You can see him there at night, surrounded by sparks; he is the moon.

The Sumu say they are the children of Papañ, engendered by his rays. And they call him Ma-Papañ, which means Sun-Papa or Sun-Father.

This story is based on the legend as given by Guida Grossman in his "Legends and Customs of the Pansamak Sumus" in *The American,* Bluefields, Nicaragua, Dec. 2, 1914, and outlined in Eduard Conzemius: *Ethnographical Survey of the Miskito and Sumu Indians of Honduras and Nicaragua.*

V
South American Indian

FOLLOWERS OF
THE GOLDEN ROD

THE ORIGIN MYTH of the ancient Incas of Peru has two beginnings. One says that our father, the Sun, created the world and the heavenly bodies and formed mankind out of clay. And he was moved with pity when he looked down upon the earth and saw the people living naked, shivering in the cold, and not knowing how to spin or weave or how to plant seeds or use the wonderful plants around them. So he sent his own son and daughter into the world and said, "Give the people this maize and tell them to plant it. Give them potatoes. Give them houses and flocks of llamas, and teach them how to weave cotton and wool for their comfort."

He placed the boy and girl in Lake Titicaca and said, "Roam as you please, but at every resting-place thrust this staff into the ground."

This was a golden rod, eighteen inches long. Wherever it sank into the ground by itself at the first thrust, there they were to settle and establish a city. "Teach the people how to live," he said, "and tell them to be as benevolent as your father, the Sun."

The early pre-Inca people called their creator, the Sun, by the name of Pachacamac. The Incas called him

Viracocha, the Uncreated Creator, Ancient Foundation, Lord, and Teacher of the World. He existed ages before the Incas existed, and they received him, the unknown, mysterious god, from the people before them. No man ever saw him—only his works. And they used to cry out to him, "Where art thou?", praying to be shown where he was, seeking his comfort.

The second beginning of the Inca origin myth begins on a hill. Paccari-tambo, the Tavern of the Dawn, was the name of three caves in the side of that hill.

Out of the center cave came four brothers, all named Ayar: Ayar-manco, the princely one, their leader; Ayar-auca, the fighter; Ayar-cachi, the salt one; and Ayar-oco, the pepper Ayar. With them emerged the four Mamas, their sister-wives: Mama-occlo, the pure; Mama-huaco, the warlike one; Mama-ipagora, the aunt weed; and Mama Rawa.

They said, "We are going forth to find a rich and fertile land." And out of the other two caves poured the people who followed them.

They traveled northeastward, Ayar-manco leading them with the golden staff in his hand. He possessed a wonderful falcon, also, whom he called "Brother." And as they traveled they changed the face of the earth.

Ayar-cachi, the salt Ayar, was very powerful. He could topple a mountain and fling it into a ravine. He was too strong; the brothers feared him. Finally by a ruse they got him to enter a cave in search of a treasure which was not there, and while he was inside they rolled a huge rock across the mouth of it. Ayar-cachi roared and shook the earth, but could not get out. He cursed the man that placed the rock across the cave. "Become

116

stone!" he said. This happened instantly; the man whose hand had rolled the stone became stone himself, and a big rock called the Traitor's Stone still stands beside a cave about 25 miles from Cuzco.

The Ayars went on and stopped again on the edge of the valley of Cuzco. Here on a hill they saw an idol, a sacred thing (*huaca*). Ayar-oco went to get it and was turned to stone himself as he touched it. Huanacauri was the name of that hill, and they named the stone brother Huanacauri also.

Slowly they continued their journey. The next time they stopped to rest, Ayar-manco stood on a little mound and hurled the golden rod with all his might. It flew through the air and sank into the earth three miles away.

"This is our land," they said. "This is our sign. Here is the navel of the earth. Here shall be the city."

There was a cairn, a great pile of stones, near the place, and Manco told Ayar-auca to go stand upon it and proclaim possession of the region for them all. Ayar-auca ran with joy and climbed the mound, but as he turned to face the people, he too became a stone.

This cairn was the site of the city of Cuzco. Here Manco settled, in the mountains of Peru 12,000 feet above the sea, in the fertile land between two roaring rivers. Here he and Mama-occlo were parents of a son named Sinchi Roq'a, who was the first of the royal line of Incas. Here Manco built the wonderful House of the Sun for Viracocha. And here they received the gift of fire. They received it in a little hollow mirror (or a polished concave plate) from the sun himself, and transferred the beams to a fluff of cotton wool, which immediately blazed.

117

Here in the temple of the Sun the Incas worshipped the sun and moon and stars and lightning for centuries. But Viracocha they adored above all. Some of the Inca hymns to Viracocha stand with the most beautiful poetry in the world.

> O Viracocha, Creator of the world,
> Where art thou?
> Fainting we long for thee.
> Maker of men and women,
> Giver of life, giver of valor,
> Listen from the sky—or from the sea—
> Wherever thou art.
> Comfort our weariness,
> Let us not die.

This story is based on material found in Paul Radin: *The Story of the American Indian,* New York, 1944; *Encyclopedia of Religion and Ethics* 1:469-471; Sir Clements Markham: *The Incas of Peru,* London, 1910. The hymn presented here is a composite free paraphrase of several hymns translated by Markham (above) from Mossi's edited text of *Relacion de antiguedes desta reyno di Peru* (*c.* 1620) by Juan de Santa Cruz Pachacuti-Yamqui Salcamayhua in *Rites and Laws of the Yncas,* London, 1873.

MBIR

WATER AND BULLRUSHES came first and the worm Mbir was crawling around on the bullrushes. After a while Mbir took the shape of man, and in this shape he created the world.

Later the people called him Miracucha. With Miracucha they named two other gods: Zaguagua, the Sun, whose headdress is so bright that men cannot look at it except when Zaguagua is low in the west; and Abaangui, who kept trying to become a man. At last he got himself into human shape, but his nose was so monstrous that he had to take it off. It flew into the sky—and there it is—the moon.

Tamoi was the First Ancestor: Tamoi, whom the people still call Grandfather. He taught them everything they know about planting seeds and gathering the fruits of the earth. He showed them how to make *chicha*, the good Indian beer, out of maize and sweet manioc. He gave them their bows and arrows and taught them to shoot fish with the arrows, and how to set basket-traps for fish in their river dams, and how to spear an eel. And he showed them how to make fire by twisting an arrow shaft on a flat piece of bamboo wood.

After his work was done Tamoi transformed his wife and baby into rocks, which are landmarks yet, and went off into the west.

Some people think that Grandfather Tamoi, the First Ancestor, is the same god as Miracucha, who was first of all Mbir, the creator worm. For when a man's soul travels to the Happy Land of the Grandfather in the west, it meets the huge Grandfather of Worms in the path, who becomes smaller and smaller and lets the soul pass if it is a good soul, but grows bigger and bigger and splits the wicked ones.

After Tamoi vanished from the world, the people danced and sang for Tamoi. The songs ask the flowers to bloom for Tamoi, the birds to spread their colored feathers and sing for Tamoi, the trees to sprout with green for Tamoi. "Everything make Tamoi look upon the world," they sing, for the people still pray to Tamoi for food and happiness and have never prayed in vain.

This is the creation myth of the Guarayú-Guaraní Indians of eastern Bolivia, retold from the fragments presented by Alfred Métraux in the *Handbook of South American Indians,* vol. 3, 437*f.*

OUR GREAT FATHER

IN THE BEGINNING there was only empty darkness
and in the dark the Eternal Bats fought eternally together. In the empty darkness Our Great Father found
himself. He found and knew himself to be the sun, and
then he made this earth and propped it up on the Eternal
Cross.

Our Great Father then made a woman and called her
Our Mother. In time Our Mother gave birth to twins,
Our Elder Brother and Our Younger Brother. These
two began to finish and improve the world as soon as they
were able.

Most of the Guaraní Indians say that Our Elder
Brother is the Sun, beneficent and creative, and Our
Younger Brother is the Moon, weak and stupid. He
went blundering around, making mistakes which Elder

Brother had to undo and set right after him. Our Great Father is the Sun also, but he is thought of as the Sun itself, high in the heaven, caring for mankind but far, far off, as distinct from the light and warmth of the sun which touch the earth. Our Great Father also had a son named Tupã, who is the thunder. His name means the Big Noise.

Our Elder Brother stole fire from the vultures and gave it to mankind, and he taught the people all their medicine dances.

Whenever there is an eclipse of the sun or moon the people think that Our Great Father has let loose the Eternal Bats to attack them, or the Celestial Jaguar to devour them. The Apapocuva say that this world will end soon. Our Great Father will pull out the props from behind the world; it will burn up in a great fire, and the Eternal Bats and the Celestial Jaguar will destroy the stars.

This is the creation story of the Apapocuva-Guaraní Indians of Brazil, based on the material presented by Alfred Métraux in his article "The Guaraní" in the *Handbook of South American Indians,* vol. 3, 92f.

MAN EMERGES

KARUSAKAIBÖ made the world one day, but he did not get as far as making mankind. Karusakaibö was alone in the world except for Daiiru, the Armadillo, who was his helper and companion.

One day Daiiru offended the creator in some way, and Karusakaibö was so enraged that Daiiru hid in a hole in the ground. Karusakaibö knew he was in there. He blew into the hole with a great gust of wind and stamped his foot upon the earth with such force that Daiiru was blown out of the hole into the air.

When he landed on the earth he said, "There are people down there!"

"What?" said Karusakaibö.

"There are people down there, living under the earth," said Daiiru.

"We must get them out," said Karusakaibö.

123

So Karusakaibö and Daiiru went to work and made a cotton rope. They beat the raw cotton with sticks to separate the fibers and they twisted the thread to make a long, strong rope, which they let down into the hole. And Daiiru went down first to show them how.

The people began to climb out. They climbed up the rope one by one, but many, many came out. When half of them had climbed out into the world, the rope broke and the rest had to stay underground. They are there yet. The sun shines in their country when it is night in this world, but of course it travels from west to east down there. The moon shines there whenever it is absent from the skies we see.

One version of this story says that the place where Karusakaibö stamped his foot is in the village of Necodemos. There the people climbed up the rope from the underworld, and the Mundurucú Indians are the ones whom Karusakaibö tattooed to look like himself. The rest, some white, some black, ran off in different directions.

Karusakaibö then gave the Mundurucú the gifts of life: he showed them how to plant maize and manioc and how to bake manioc meal, and he showed them how to spin raw cotton. The petroglyphs on the cliffs near Necodemos are said to be the work of Karusakaibö.

This is the creation myth of the Mundurucú Indians of Brazil, based on the material presented by Donald Horton in his article "The Mundurucú" in the *Handbook of South American Indians*, vol. 3, 281*f*.

IT WAS THERE

THE CUBEO INDIANS in southeastern Colombia do not believe that the world was ever created. It was there. There was no creator, they say, because nobody could make a river or a forest or a sun or a moon.

Who could make a river? The rivers were always there. Who could make a sun or a moon? These things have existed forever.

The Cubeo themselves were the first people. They call themselves *pámiwa*, first people, or The Ancients. But nobody made them. They came forth out of the rocks in the roaring rapids at three places along the river Vaupas.

They came out two by two, as anacondas, and when they shed their skins they were people. They settled here and there up and down the rivers and never went into the forests. The forest (*maqáno*) was mysterious and unknown to them. They did not enter.

The Cubeo have a word for the great god who lives in the sky; *Hümene hinkü*, they call him, which means "my little spirit." The spirits of the dead go to the sky to Hümene hinkü, the people say, and are allowed to remain if they pay (even little children have to pay), but they do not live in the house with the god; they live out in his dog-house.

Quwai is the god they supplicate, for Quwai is the one who put the fish in the rivers so that the people would not starve.

Quwai gave the people manioc and fruits and taught them how to plant and hoe, and how to weave hammocks out of palm fiber. He made hordes of little flies to bite the people and make them jump and run from place to place, and not be lazy. And he taught them how to mourn for their dead and how to make the mourning masks.

All the creatures in the world come to the aid of the mourners whenever there is a death. All the animals, the birds, the fishes, and the insects are portrayed by the masked dancers of the mourning rite.

Avya is the man in the sky who gives light; he is the sun and the moon: one, not two. He walks across the sky all day giving light for the work that must be done in the world. At night he gives less light so the people may sleep. Whenever there is an eclipse, the people say, "Avya is dying," and they rush out of their houses shouting and searching for the ill-willed medicine man whom they hold responsible.

This story is adapted from information gathered by Irving Goodman from one group of Cubeo Indians living along the Cuduiari River in southeastern Colombia in 1939-1940, and presented in his article, "Cosmological Beliefs of the Cubeo Indians," in the *Journal of American Folklore*, 53:242-247.

THE WORM TURNED

DOBITT is the name of the creator of the Mosetene Indians who live on the eastern slopes of the Andes in Bolivia. Dobitt created the world. He made it in the shape of a great raft, which floats in space supported by innumerable spirits.

Then Dobitt created mankind to live in the world. He made images out of clay and gave them life, and then went off to live in the sky.

After a while he sent Keri as a white condor into the world to see how mankind was getting along. Dobitt let him down from the sky with a rope, but the rope broke and Keri was killed. So Dobitt created fish out of the condor's head.

Then Dobitt himself came into the world and created animals and birds. He carried a big basket full of water and spilled it out here and there over the earth to make the rivers. He gave mankind agriculture and taught men all they know of planting yams and maize and manioc and harvesting bananas and other fruits. He taught them how to travel the rivers on rafts, how to weave mats of reeds or leaves for their beds, and how to make mosquito nets.

The Mosetene say that the Milky Way is an enormous worm. A man picked it up for a pet one day when it was little, but it grew and grew, until too many animals had to be killed to feed it, and after a while, too many men. The people got tired of this and finally killed its owner. So the worm turned and devoured its master's murderers and then went off into the sky.

The Mosetene also have a story saying that once the sky fell down upon the earth. A huge serpent put it back and still holds it there with the arch of his back. But nobody remembers when this happened.

This is the creation myth of the Mosetene Indians based on the material presented by Alfred Métraux in his article "Tribes of the Eastern Slopes of the Bolivian Andes" in the *Handbook of South American Indians,* vol. 3, 503f.

AT WORLD'S END

AT THE VERY SOUTHERN tip of South America lies the end of the world: Tierra del Fuego, Land of Fire. It is an archipelago of big and little islands separated from the mainland by the Strait of Magellan. Ferdinand Magellan, the Portuguese explorer, discovered it in November, 1520, and described it as "a forbidding land, stark with eternal cold." He named it the Land of Fire for the many fires which he saw burning on the shores, for every family there had a fire in front of its dwelling. Perhaps he saw the canoe fires also, for the Yahgan people carry fire in their canoes.

The people are the Ona, the Yahgan, and the Alacaluf Indians. The Ona live on the island of Tierra del Fuego and are called Foot Indians, or Land People, because they do not use canoes. The Yahgan and Alacaluf are called Canoe Indians. The Yahgan are the southernmost people in the world, occupying the southern coast of Tierra del Fuego island and all the little islands southward to Cape Horn. The Alacaluf probably got their name from the Yahgan, who call them *Innalum Aala Kaluf*, the "western men with the mussel-shell knives." They occupy the western islands.

The Tierra del Fuego Indians have been called the most primitive, the least advanced of all the people in the world, and "without religion." Yet long before there were any missionaries among them, or any outside contact or influence, these people worshipped an invisible supreme god, whom they thought of as living in the sky.

The supreme god of the Ona was Témaukl', whom they called That One There Above, or The One in the Sky. The Yahgan say My Father, or The Old One, The Good One, or The Strong One, or (when they are stricken with grief for a death) The Murderer in the Sky. The Alacaluf call their high god Xél'ás, the Star. Both the Ona and the Alacaluf regard their supreme gods as creators of the universe.

Témaukl' always existed, the Ona say. He created the sky and the earth, and there was no time when Témaukl' was not. He had the giving of life and the giving of death, and sometimes punished the people by sending epidemics.

Kenos was the first man, sent into the world by Témaukl' to put things in order. So Kenos created the

130

plants and animals and gave the Ona their own land. K'aux came after him; he was the mythical hero who divided the land into 39 hunting sections and assigned each Ona family to one of them. North and South were two important characters in Ona mythology. They kept struggling for power. Sometimes one would win, sometimes the other. And they are still at it, for sometimes the terrible antarctic cold prevails, and sometimes it gets a little warmer for the Ona.

The people have always felt that Témaukl' was far, far away, yet whoever ate meat late at night threw a small piece out of the hut, saying, "This is for the One Above." And during bitter storm and snow, a little piece of glowing coal was faithfully put outside for Témaukl' with a prayer for better weather.

Xé'lás, the Star, the creator god of the Alacaluf, also lives in the sky, and watches what men do. He puts the soul in the newborn baby and takes it back at the proper time.

The great god of the Yahgan, named Watauinéwa, owned the world but did not create it. He gave mankind animals and plants and the spark of life and their moral code. And as giver of life, he took it back whenever he pleased. Evil-doers always died young. The Yahgan prayed to him daily. The prayers were formulas of praise or thanksgiving, requests for food or cure or protection, or words of complaint and reproach for sickness, bad weather, and death.

VI
Africa

MBERE'S MAN

MBERE, the creator, made a man out of clay, but first he was a lizard. Mbere put the lizard in the great big sea water. He left him there five days. On the fifth day Mbere looked and the lizard was in there. On the seventh day Mbere looked and the lizard was in there. On the eighth day Mbere looked and the lizard came out. But when he came out he was a man. "Thank you," said the man to Mbere.

This is the creation story of the Fans, a western Bantu people of French Equatorial Africa. See the *Standard Dictionary of Folklore, Mythology, and Legend,* 697.

At the top of the page is a wood carving of an "ancestor head" of the Fan people, drawn from a photograph in P. Radin and J. J. Sweeney: *African Folktales and Sculpture.*

TOO BIG

MAWU is the creator god of the Negro people of Dahomey in West Africa. Mawu is the moon, mother of the gods and of the world, mother of mankind, and the giver of souls to the newborn.

Mawu is one or Mawu is two: Mawu is the great mother who created the world, or Mawu is Mawu-Lisa, male and female, father-mother of the universe. Mawu is the moon in the sky or Mawu is Mawu-Lisa, moon *and* sun, over the world.

But it was Mawu who created the universe. And as she went around creating the universe, she rode on the back of Aido Hwedo, the great rainbow serpent who was so big he could encircle the sky.

Every morning, wherever Mawu and Aido Hwedo had spent the night, mountains stood; in whatever place the great serpent had lain coiled, the mountains rose and towered.

When the world was finished, they soon saw that too many things were too big. The earth itself was too big; it was heavy. Mawu saw that it would surely topple.

So she said, "Coil around the earth and steady it."

And Aido Hwedo coiled around the earth.

"Bear its weight," said Mawu. And Aido Hwedo tightened up a little.

Aido Hwedo encircles the earth today. And to keep himself from slipping, he holds the tip of his tail in his mouth. He cannot bear the heat of the sun, so Mawu caused the sea to rise around him for his dwelling-place. He arches across the sky from edge to edge and around the whole curve of the earth below. And his body lies in the sea. Once in a while he gets tired and uncomfortable and shifts a little to ease himself, and then there is an earthquake in the world.

Some day he will get hungry and begin to swallow his tail. And on that day the world will fall into the sea.

Mawu is never reproduced by image or symbol but the name of Mawu is on the tongue of every man every day. He does not say "By God!" he says "in the name of our mother Mawu" when he wants to emphasize some solemn statement.

Ask any Dahomean who created the world and he will say Mawu was mother and creatrix of the world.

"But who created Mawu?" he will ask back. There was another god, named Nana Buluku with power great enough to create Mawu.

"And this one, Nana Buluku, the creator of Mawu, was the Great Creator, then?"

"No man knows," is the answer. "This power also must have had its own creator." And so the Dahomean mind reaches back into the unthinkable past.

This story is based on the material presented and analyzed by Melville J. Herskovits in *Dahomey: An Ancient West African Kingdom,* vol. 2, 289-292.

Obassi Osaw

and Obassi Nsi

OBASSI OSAW and Obassi Nsi were the first gods. They lived together in the beginning of the world, and walked together, and made all things together. But after a while Obassi Osaw went off to live in the sky and Obassi Nsi chose to dwell in the earth.

The Ekoi people say that Obassi Nsi has the most power, because every child that is born falls upon the earth and every man that dies goes into the earth. Obassi Nsi is the kind and giving god. He gives mankind his crops.

Obassi Osaw is the sky god whose eyes are the stars. He sends rain, but he often sends too much.

One day in the beginning of the world Obassi Osaw made a man and a woman and brought them down to live upon the earth. He placed them here in the green world and then went back to the sky.

After a while he came back to see how they were getting along.

138

"What have you eaten? What have you had to drink?" Obassi asked them.

"Nothing."

Then Obassi dug a ditch and from a fold in his great blue robe he drew forth a jar full of water and poured the water into the ditch. This was the first river.

The next thing he did was to plant a palm kernel which he carried in his hand.

"Drink the water. Wash in the water. Cook your food in water," said Obassi to the man and woman. "Take care of the palm tree."

So the man and woman watched the palm tree grow and tended it with care and love. After a while great clusters of yellow fruit ripened.

When Obassi saw this, "This is your food," he said to the man and woman. "Eat the outer rind." So the people used the outer rind of the fruits for their daily food.

"The kernel makes good medicine," said Obassi. And thus Obassi gave mankind water, food, and medicine.

This story is based on the discussions of the concepts of creation and the creation tales of the Ekoi people of southeastern Nigeria in P. Amaury Talbot: *In the Shadow of the Bush,* 70f., 373-374.

ZAMBE

IN THE EARLY DAYS of the world, Zambe, son of Mebe'e, made a man and named him Zambe. Then he made a chimpanzee and named him Zambe, a gorilla named Zambe, and an elephant, Zambe. He made two men, one white and one black, and named them both Zambe. And he gave each of them gifts to help them live their lives in the world: fire, water, knives, hoes, axes, and a book. Then Zambe went away.

The two men sat by the fire. But the smoke got in the white man's eyes, so he took his book and walked away. That is all he took—the book.

The chimpanzee looked about and saw great clusters of fruit ripening in a high tree. So he dropped his knife and his hoe and his ax and his book and turned his back on the fire, and went and ate the fruit. When Gorilla saw Chimpanzee eating the luscious fruit, he did the same. The elephant had plenty of everything and did not bother about anything.

The black man stirred up the fire and kept it going; he was so busy, he did not read the book.

When Zambe came back he called them all to him and said, "Where are the things?"

Chimpanzee said, "I dropped my things when I went to eat the fruit."

"Go get them!"

Chimpanzee searched and searched but he could never find them.

"So you shall live in the forests forever," said Zambe. And he sprinkled hair all over the chimpanzee, put some great big teeth in his mouth, and let him go.

"Now, you?" said Zambe to Gorilla.

"I left my things when I went to eat the fruit."

"You shall be like Chimpanzee." So the gorilla went off into the forest.

Then Zambe looked at the black man.

"Where is your book?" he said.

"I have not read the book. I was tending the fire," said the black man named Zambe.

"Ah, you are without knowledge," said Zambe the god. "Go on tending the fire. You will have to work for everything."

Then Zambe said to the white man, "All the days of your life you will never put down the book, because it is the only thing you chose. You will have understanding, but you will have to live without fire unless some black man makes it for you."

Thus Chimpanzee, Gorilla, and Elephant live in the forests because they did not take care of Zambe's gifts. White men have plenty of book-learning; and black men work for a living and enjoy a warm fire.

This story explaining the division of gifts and labor between white man and black sounds odd to us today. But it was in keeping with the way the Bulu people sized up human economy in (German) Kamerun when this story was first told by a black man to a white man in 1882. Rewritten from the tale as told by Adolf N. Krug: "Bulu Tales from Kamerun, West Africa," *Journal of American Folklore* 25:111 (1912).

CHAMELEON FINDS

AT FIRST there were no people. Only Mulungu and the decent peaceful beasts were in the world.

One day Chameleon sat weaving a fish-trap, and when he had finished he set it in the river. In the morning he pulled the trap and it was full of fish, which he took home and ate.

He set the trap again. In the morning he pulled it out and it was empty: no fish.

"Bad luck," he said, and set the trap again.

The next morning when he pulled the trap he found a little man and woman in it. He had never seen any creatures like this.

"What can they be?" he said. "Today I behold the unknown." And he picked up the fish-trap and took the two creatures to Mulungu.

"Father," said Chameleon, "see what I have brought."

Mulungu looked. "Take them out of the trap," he said. "Put them down on the earth and they will grow."

Chameleon did this. And the man and woman grew. They grew until they became as tall as men and women are today.

All the animals watched to see what the people would do. They made fire. They rubbed two sticks together in a special way and thus made fire. The fire caught in the bush and roared through the forest and the animals had to run to escape the flames.

The people caught a buffalo and killed it and roasted it in the fire and ate it. Then next day they did the same thing. Every day they set fires and killed some animal and ate it.

"They are burning up everything!" said Mulungu. "They are killing my people!"

All the beasts ran into the forest as far away from mankind as they could get. Chameleon went into the high trees.

"I'm leaving!" said Mulungu.

He called to Spider. "How do you climb on high?" he said.

"Very nicely," said Spider. And Spider spun a rope for Mulungu and Mulungu climbed the rope and went to live in the sky.

Thus the gods were driven off the face of the earth by the cruelty of man.

This story, told by the Yao people who live along the shores of Lake Nyasa in northern Mozambique, is rewritten from Duff Macdonald's literal transcription of it as told to him and published in his *Africana: The Heart of Heathen Africa,* vol. 1, 295f.

FROM BUMBA

IN THE BEGINNING, in the dark, there was nothing but water. And Bumba was alone.

One day Bumba was in terrible pain. He retched and strained and vomited up the sun. After that light spread over everything. The heat of the sun dried up the water until the black edges of the world began to show. Black sandbanks and reefs could be seen. But there were no living things.

Bumba vomited up the moon and then the stars, and after that the night had its own light also.

Still Bumba was in pain. He strained again and nine living creatures came forth: the leopard named Koy Bumba, and Pongo Bumba the crested eagle, the crocodile, Ganda Bumba, and one little fish named Yo; next, old Kono Bumba, the tortoise, and Tsetse, the lightning, swift, deadly, beautiful like the leopard, then the white

145

heron, Nyanyi Bumba, also one beetle, and the goat named Budi.

Last of all came forth men. There were many men, but only one was white like Bumba. His name was Loko Yima.

The creatures themselves then created all the creatures. The heron created all the birds of the air except the kite. He did not make the kite. The crocodile made serpents and the iguana. The goat produced every beast with horns. Yo, the small fish, brought forth all the fish of all the seas and waters. The beetle created insects.

Then the serpents in their turn made grasshoppers, and the iguana made the creatures without horns.

Then the three sons of Bumba said they would finish the world. The first, Nyonye Ngana, made the white ants; but he was not equal to the task, and died of it. The ants, however, thankful for life and being, went searching for black earth in the depths of the world and covered the barren sands to bury and honor their creator.

Chonganda, the second son, brought forth a marvelous living plant from which all the trees and grasses and flowers and plants in the world have sprung. The third son, Chedi Bumba, wanted something different, but for all his trying made only the bird called the kite.

Of all the creatures Tsetse, lightning, was the only troublemaker. She stirred up so much trouble that Bumba chased her into the sky. Then mankind was without fire until Bumba showed the people how to draw fire out of trees. "There is fire in every tree," he told them, and showed them how to make the firedrill and liberate it. Sometimes today Tsetse still leaps down and strikes the earth and causes damage.

146

When at last the work of creation was finished, Bumba walked through the peaceful villages and said to the people, "Behold these wonders. They belong to you." Thus from Bumba, the Creator, the First Ancestor, came forth all the wonders that we see and hold and use, and all the brotherhood of beasts and man.

Translated and adapted from the creation story of the Boshongo people of the Belgian Congo as presented in E. Torday and T. A. Joyce: *Les Boshongo,* 20*f.*

UNKULUNKULU

UNKULUNKULU, the Old-Old One, the creator, is no longer known: so say the Zulu people. He was the first man; he *broke off* in the beginning. He broke off from a bed of reeds, from *uthlanga*, the jointed reed which reproduces by offshoots and thus has become synonymous with the concept of source.

Unkulunkulu broke off, and he in turn broke off the people from *uthlanga*. And after mankind was broken off, he broke off the cattle and he broke off all the children of the nations. Then he broke off doctors and gave the people medicines and dreams.

The old men say that Unkulunkulu was the first Off-breaker from the reed; and some call him *Uthlanga*, saying that he himself was the reed (source) from which all men broke off henceforth. Unkulunkulu was the first man and made the first men: so said the ancient men of long ago who witnessed the breaking off.

Those ancient men are here no more, but those begotten of them are here and say that the ancient ones knew also about the breaking off of the world. Those that are here are the Zulu people who never saw Unkulunkulu; but they have been told that Unkulunkulu existed in that place where he broke off from the reed and broke off the rest of us.

Everything was given to man in this world by Unkulunkulu. He created water and mountains and caused the trees to grow, and made the cattle, wild animals, snakes, birds, everything. He looked at the existing sun and said to the people, "It will give you light." Of the cattle he said, "These are yours. Eat the flesh and milk." He cut the little tree named *uluzi* and kindled fire by friction and told the people, "Be warm. Cook with it." And Unkulunkulu cooked the first corn and ate it himself, to show the people how. Then he looked at all the wild animals and told the people what they were. "That is an elephant," he said; "that is a buffalo," and so on.

Before there were any missionaries among the Zulu, if some one said, "Whence came the stones?" the answer would be that Unkulunkulu broke off the stones and men too from the bed of reeds. When it rains the people still say, "How the heaven of Unsondo rains!" (for Unsondo is another name for Unkulunkulu). When men digging find the earth hard, they say, "Hard is the earth of Unkulunkulu."

They say that Unkulunkulu made the rain and the corn and pointed to them, saying, "I have made these things for you that you may know me by them."

"Therefore, to us," the Zulu say, "Unkulunkulu is a stalk of corn. He is here." And sometimes they say, "We do not understand about Unkulunkulu. We know only that he gave us all things and made a path in the world for us to walk in." And he created nothing that was evil.

When the old men say that Unkulunkulu came into being and gave life to man and that he broke off from a bed of reeds, sometimes the people ask, "Where is this bed of reeds?" Many people have roamed far, here and there, looking for it. The answer is, "We do not know. We know only that the old men before us told this story and they too did not know where the reed-bed was." But they do say that it still grows in that first place, which was by the sea. Some say it was in a valley; but all say that the reed was growing in the edge of water.

As for Unkulunkulu's ever having a wife, some say yes and some say no. Some say that Unkulunkulu appeared in the world "from the other side of the rock." He created men from a bed of reeds and told them, "I, too, sprang from a bed of reeds." And they say that when he sprang out, a woman sprang out after him, and together they had but the one name: Unkulunkulu.

One version of the story is that Unkulunkulu came out of the reed-bed first, and after him a woman; then came a cow, and after it a bull; then came a bitch, and after it a dog. Then came all the little animals, then the elephants.

After that the corn grew and Unkulunkulu, the first man, said to the first woman, "Let's eat it." And the woman said, "How?"

"Cut it. Thrash it," said the man. "Find a stone. Go find another stone. Grind the corn between the stones."

150

And this has been the way of mankind with corn ever since, not only among the Zulu, but all over the world.

But whatever version of the creation story the Zulu tell, they all say that Unkulunkulu was the first man, who broke off from the reed, and he saw no one who created him.

This is a composite condensation of the several accounts of Unkulunkulu collected by Henry Callaway in his *Religious System of the Amazulu,* 1-104.

CAGN, THE MANTIS

Cagn is the name of the African Bushman creator. We see it written *!kaggen*. The exclamation mark with which it begins represents the distinctive Bushman cerebral click. Dr. W. H. I. Bleek in his notes on the Bushman language has explained, "The cerebral click ! is sounded by curling up the tip of the tongue against the roof of the mouth and withdrawing it suddenly and forcibly." The nearest we can come to pronouncing the name, however, is Cag-n. (Pronounce the *g*.)

The people believe that Cagn manifests himself in the form of a praying-mantis. (The word *!kaggen* means mantis.) When the Bushman sees a praying-mantis he says, "There goes Cagn." All Bushmen reverence the mantis; no Bushman would kill one.

CAGN created all things and used to dwell with men on this earth; but how Cagn himself came into the world no

152

one knows. He used to be a kindly god, but "he got spoiled," the people say, from having to cope with the stubbornness and opposition of mankind. He could not establish his ways in peace, so he went away. He does not like to look at the world today and what goes on in it. But the people still pray to him for food, saying, "Cagn, O Cagn, do you not see the hunger of your children?"

Cagn had a wife named Coti and two sons who became great chiefs. These two made digging sticks with sharp stone points, and went around showing the people how to dig with them for roots to eat. His daughter married a snake, and snakes henceforth were called Cagn's people.

Cagn could change himself into any animal form. Sometimes he was a mantis, but often he was an eland bull. Cagn loved the elands. And today no man knows where Cagn is; only the elands know. When Cagn calls in the forest, all the elands run to him. Men have seen the elands raise their heads, hearing some call which men cannot hear, and run to it. This is one way Cagn protects the elands from mankind.

Once Cagn, going along in the darkness, threw his shoe into the sky to be the moon. And the moon shining in the night makes enough light for travelers. Some of the Bushman stories say that the moon "walks in the night and feels that he is a shoe."

But Cagn did not put the sun in the sky. That happened another way. The sun was once a man who lived on earth. He was left-handed because from his right armpit shown forth a great light. If he put down his arm, darkness fell everywhere; when he lifted it up, it was like day. But the greatest of his light and warmth, of course, fell around his own house. And when he lay down to sleep, all others in that village were cold in the dark.

So the women got together and told the children, "Go watch Old Man Armpit, and when he lies asleep take hold of him all together and throw him into the sky." Carefully one old white-headed woman gave the children their instructions. "Grasp him firmly, all together, and throw him up," she said, "but speak to him as you throw and tell him he must altogether become the sun, to go forward and pass along the sky and be hot so that the Bushman rice may dry."

So the children went and sat by Old Man Armpit's house, and when the old man fell asleep, they saw that the light from his armpit made just a little spread of light upon the ground. All together they stood around him and grasped him firmly and threw him into the sky, saying, "O Grandfather Armpit, become the Sun, which is hot, so that the Bushman rice may dry, so that thou makest the whole earth warm and light. Thou must altogether shine, taking away darkness."

The children then went home and said that it was done. And the story as the Bushmen tell it says, "The sun comes; the darkness goes away; the sun sets, darkness comes; the moon comes at night. Day breaks; the sun comes; darkness goes away; the sun sets; darkness comes; the moon brightens the darkness." The moon, Cagn's shoe, goes along in the night, taking away the darkness.

But the Sun, when he got into the sky, drove the Moon away. He went after it with a knife and cut and cut and cut.

"O Sun! leave for the children the backbone!" Moon

cried. So the Sun consented and left Moon his backbone. Sometimes that is the way people see him, just his thin backbone in the sky, curved like Cagn's shoe. And the moon thus is a new moon, but knows he will be whole again. He puts on a new stomach; he grows large again; he is whole, and goes by night, feeling that he is Cagn's shoe which walks in the sky by night.

This story is a composite of several Bushman myths and folk-tales. See article "Cagn" in *Standard Dictionary of Folklore, Mythology, and Legend,* and W. H. I. Bleek and L. C. Lloyd: *Specimens of Bushman Folklore.*

VII
Oceania

Indonesia—Polynesia—Melanesia—Micronesia—Australia

THE OUTBURSTERS

"GOOD is the island of Yami," said the god, looking down at the flat world, and dropped a big stone on the spot which is now the village of Ipaptok. The village is named that because there grows the bean-bearing plant called *paptok*, which the first man used for food.

The big stone fell upon Ipaptok, and out of it burst a man. He was hungry when he first came out and ate the *paptok*. Then he walked down to the sea.

He saw that a bamboo was growing by the sea, and as he watched, it split and out burst another man.

"Who are we?" said one. "We are man," said the other.

The son of the bamboo walked in one direction and found silver at a place named Kasavilugan. The son of the stone walked in another direction and found iron at a place named Imasapau. They returned to their house and beat out the hard iron and the soft silver.

159

One day the right knee-joint of the son of bamboo swelled and itched and a boy child burst out; from the left knee-joint came a girl child. The same thing happened to the son of stone: from his right knee burst out a boy child; from his left knee came a girl.

These children grew up and married. The daughter of the son of stone wed the son of the son of bamboo, and happy generations followed.

The people built themselves canoes. But the son of bamboo could not fell the heavy trees with his silver ax. "Hand me the iron," he said, "to cut the heavy tree." So the people learned that the silver ax was too soft for hewing wood, but because they loved the silver, they made themselves silver helmets. Today they wear the silver helmets adorned with beautiful silver leaf-shapes when they launch the canoes for the Flying-fish Festival and perform the fish-calling ceremony.

They built canoes and launched them with song. They were very beautiful, carved with trees and waves, and painted with black and white and red. The son of stone fixed ribs on the outside of his canoe; the son of bamboo put ribs on the inside of his. When the canoe of the son of bamboo was pushed into the sea, it broke. When the canoe of the son of stone entered the sea, it leaked. "That's bad," he said. Quickly he looked for something to plug the leaks and chose the fiber of the *kulau* tree. When the leaks were stopped, "Mended," he said. And the people use this fiber today to plug a leak.

Thus the people learned to make canoes and become fishermen. Every year during the season of flying-fish, they hold their Flying-fish Festival. At this time no one will offend the wonderful fish by spitting in the sea or

160

throwing stones in the water. They fish at night by torchlight with torches in the end of each canoe. They perform the sacred fish-calling ceremony, and sing this song:

From Ipaptok, the place of the outbursting of man,
The first one descended to the plain of the sea.
He performed the fish-calling rite;
The torch was lighted: and the fish
Were dazzled by the flames.

This is the creation myth of the Yami, an Indonesian people on the island of Botel-Tobago, a tiny coral island off the southeastern tip of Formosa. This story is based on Arundel Del Re's *Creation Myths of the Formosan Natives*.

Here is the Yami cosmos the way Yami artists themselves depict it, divided into nine planes.

At the very top of the universe are the three great gods, or *anitos*, who send thunder, lightning, rain. The one to the left is the Great God; the one in the middle is the storm god; the one

to the right is his son, so lazy that his father makes him roll around the world. This, the Yami say, is what makes the noise of thunder.

Next down, in plane 2, are the *tau-rô-tô,* the human supernaturals who live in the sky. These are the beneficent pair, male and female, who taught the Yami people how to build houses of bamboo, and how to weave cloth, and how to eat with silver spoons.

Next down (plane 3) are the shaggy-headed, pot-bellied supernaturals (*anitos*) who won't work. They come to earth and steal food from the Yami in the shape of rats.

Plane 4 is occupied by a group of goddesses called *pi-na-lung-ao* who watch over birth and newborn babies.

Next down (plane 5) is the face of this earth, occupied by the Yami themselves. Two islands show in the picture, which are perhaps Formosa and its neighbor, Kashoto Island. The Yami do not picture themselves shaggy-haired and pot-bellied like the *anitos,* but round-faced and slender-bodied like their ancestors, the *tau-rô-tô* in plane 2.

Next (plane 6) come the spirit doubles of the Yami people (also called *anitos*) who sometimes appear on earth in the shape of birds or insects.

Next down (planes 7 and 8) is the World of Men. This is divided into two parts, an upper and a lower world. The entrance to the lower world can be plainly seen in the middle. The couple to the right in the lower half represent two Yami, a brother and sister, who visited this lower world and found abundant food and peace and riches there. There are houses in both the upper and lower world.

At the bottom (plane 9) are the five huge tree trunks which support the Yami universe and the world serpent Kamurai who causes earthquakes and ocean storms when he coils and uncoils himself.

FIRST NOSES

This story about the first two people is a Bagobo folk-tale from Mindanao Island in the Philippines.

IN THE BEGINNING there was Melu in the sky—a big white god with gold teeth. He was proud of his whiteness and kept rubbing his skin to keep it white.

The old dead skin that rubbed off he put in a heap; and when he had enough he made the earth out of it. There was some left over, so he made two living creatures, just like himself only smaller.

He finished one, all but the nose. Then he finished the other, all but the nose.

While he was considering these, his stupid brother came along.

"Let me make the noses," he said. "You've had all the fun. Let me make the noses."

Melu didn't like it. He did not want to let this clumsy brother make the noses, but he finally consented. So the stupid brother made the noses. But when he put them on the faces, he got them on upside down. Then he went off.

One day it began to rain in the new world, and it rained very hard. The two people were very uncomfortable because the rain ran off their straight black hair right into the upside-down noses.

All they could do was stand on their heads. So they stood on their heads under a big tree till the rain was over.

One day when Melu noticed that there was a specially fine rain falling on the earth, he thought he would look and see if the two people were thankful for it and enjoying it, as they should be.

So he looked—and there were the two little figures standing on their heads under a tree.

"What are you doing like this?" he demanded, and turned them right side up.

At once he saw that the rain was running into their noses. He almost laughed at their ridiculous plight, but he set things right at once.

He took off the two upside-down noses and fixed them right end up—the way noses are today.

KUMULIPO or

BEGINNING-IN-DEEP-DARKNESS

Here is the beautiful creation prayer chant of the
Polynesian people of Hawaii, beginning in deep darkness and moving from the first murky ferment of life to
the dawn of the dog and the day of the appearance of
man. The original is a poem of more than 2000 lines,
recording the genealogies of the kings. It used to be
chanted for the birth of every royal child, uniting him
not only with the blood and bone that begot him and the
named generations of his ancestors, but recognizing him

also as a child of the plants and animals which first came to life in the world, as one with those crawlers who crawled out of the sea to live on earth, as one with the earth itself, and with that mysterious germ which made its first slow stirring in deep darkness: this is the genealogy of life.

THERE WAS a time when there was only night and darkness, darkness that gave forth black darkness, night that gave forth deeper night.

In this time the earth became hot; the heavens swirled and turned. The Pleiades rose in the night. And slime was the source of the earth.

In the night Kumulipo was born, a male, Kumulipo, the Source-of-deep-darkness; and Po'ele was born, a female, Po'ele whose name was Darkness. These were the parents of all hard-shelled things that came into being in the sea in the darkness and of all plant life. The coral was the first living creature, and the first stone. The grub came forth that digs and heaps up little mounds of dirt; and his child the earthworm was born. The starfish came forth, and his child, the little starfish, was born.

The barnacle was born, and the oyster; the mussel was born; the hermit crab came forth. The big limpet was born and his child the small limpet. The shellfish, the rock oyster, the clam, the sea snail, the conch, and the small conch child where born in the night.

Moss was born, living in the sea; ferns grew, living in the land. Earth and water were food for the plants, for the seagrass, the seaweeds, for the landgrass, for the mints which came forth from the land.

The god might enter this vast time and place, but not yet man. Darkness slipped into light, but it was still night.

The man with the water gourd was a god, Kane-i-ka-wai-ola. He gave water to the plants; the withered vine grew green. The long night was fruitful; the long night passed, but still it was night.

Pouliuli, the male, was born, Pouliuli, Deep-profound-darkness; born was the female, Powehiwehi, whose name means Darkness-streaked-with-glimmering-light. These two were parents of all the fish and creatures of the ocean.

The waters floated. The fish were born; porpoises were swimming in the sea. The child of the *hilu* fish swam and rested and spread his tail-fin. The shark swam forth and the sturgeon; the eel and the ray and the octopus were swimming here and there. The albacore, the mackerel, and the squid were born to swim in the sea water. The pickerel was living in the sea. The gourd vine, the taro, and the yam flourished on the land. Rushes abounded; the sandalwood and hibiscus lived and grew. The fish were swarming in the waters. They swam, rising, jerking, diving, each one swallowing, swallowing as he went. Dark was the ocean. It was still night.

Darkness hung over the sea and the land; darkness shadowed the streams and the mountains. Darkness still covered the dimly brightening night.

Po'el'ele, the male, was born, Po'el'ele, Dark-night; born was Pohaha, the female, whose name means Night-just-breaking-into-dawn. These two were parents of all tiny frail and flitting things which came to being in the

ever-lessening night. The rootstalk sprouted nine leaves;
the taro grew.

The wood-borer was born and its child was a flying
thing. The caterpillar was born and its child, the moth,
flew forth. The ant was born; the dragonfly flew over
land and stream; the grasshopper leaped about; out
came fly, the child of the worm.

The egg was born and its child was a bird: the snipe,
the plover, the flycatcher, the crow came forth from the
eggs and flew about. The little brown creeper flew; the
curlew and its child, the stilt, were born. The frigate-
bird and the albatross flew out.

The heron came into the world and flew about the sea-
shore in great flocks and settled down on the beaches.
The duck of the islands lived beside the sea; the wild
duck and the goose and the owl lived on the land.

The earth was covered with young birds in the night
that was just breaking into dawn. It was time for the
dawn but it was still night.

Popanopano, the male, was born; born was Polalowehi,
the female. This was the time when the crawlers came out
of the sea and took to the land. This was the time of the
egg-layers. The sea crept up upon the land, slipped
back, rushed forward; the crawlers advanced and produced eggs.

So were born in the night the rough-backed turtles,
the dark-red turtles, the horn-billed turtles, and the little
lobsters. The slow and slippery geckos were born, and
other creatures, fat and mud-dwelling, leaving tracks
upon the ground, creeping and crawling and poking
about.

The time came at last for Po-kanokano, the male, the Nightdigger, and Po-lalo-uli, the female, to produce.

Then in the night world the pig child, Kamapua'a, was born and went to live inland in the bush. Dark was the skin of the new generation. The nose of the beautiful black pig dug into the land and heaped it up; he cultivated the taro patches and the increase of the land was tenfold; the land sprang into bloom. The ancient line of the pig scattered and multiplied, and left their footprints in the rocks.

Po-hiolo, the male, was born, Po-hiolo, Night-falling-away; born was Po-ne'a-aku, the female, whose name meant Night-creeping-away. These were the parents of Pilo'i, the rat child. This was the time of the nibblers, brown-coated, the rats, with whiskers. They hid here and there in the world. They dug holes to live in, scratched in the wet earth. They ate in the uplands; they ate the new shoots of the taro, pilfered the fruits and nibbled the rinds. They were born in the dark, while the dark slipped away. But it was still night.

Po-ne'e-aku, the male, was born, Po-ne'e-aku, Night-receding; born was Po-neie-mai, the female, whose name meant Pregnant-night. These were the parents of a new, mysterious birth. The night grew less. The dark lightened. The dog was born, dark-red, brindled, hairless, pitiful in the cold without a coat, in the heat without cover. The wind was his companion.

Out of the slime came new rootlets; the leaves branched. Birth spread through the world. The dog was born while it was still night. But men were not far.

170

Po-kinikini and Po-he'enalu-mamao were parents of the next life. The night was passing and a child was born, well-formed. This was the time when men were born by the hundreds: man was born for the narrow stream; woman was born for the broad stream. They stood together; they slept together, in that calm time long ago, called Calmness. A great stillness lay about, awaiting the gods and man.

La'ila'a was born, a woman; a man was born, named Ki'i. The god was Kane. The face of the god was ruddy; dark was the face of man.

Here was the ocean edge, here the damp forests, the cold mountains. This was the time when men were born, little helpless ones, then children growing older, ever increasing.

Man spread over the land. Man was here.

It was day.

This telling is based on and greatly condensed from the first part of *The Kumulipo* as presented by M. W. Beckwith.

Ancient and Original Sayings

IN THE BEGINNING all was darkness with water everywhere. There was no light and Io dwelt alone in immensity. And out of utter darkness the voice of Io said, "Darkness, be light." And light appeared. Then he said, "Light, be dark." And again it was dark. Thus was the alternation of day and night ordained.

Io spoke again and proclaimed the dominion of light. Eternal dark was dispelled and a great brightness lay everywhere. Then Io said to the spreading waters, "Waters, separate." And the seas and oceans took their places and the tides henceforth flowed and ebbed.

"Heaven, be formed," he said; and the sky hung over the seas.

"O Great Evolver, bring forth." And the moving earth lay stretched, broad in his sight.

172

The priests of the Maru-tuahu tribes call the words of Io the "ancient and original sayings" which caused the birth of light and of the earth. And the words of Io which caused the light are often repeated to the very ill, or to those who are despondent, or to the aged.

When the waters drew apart, each into its own ocean, and the sky hung over the moving earth, then did Io reproduce himself in the persons of the gods. Io, Causer of motion and space and moving earth, the Great Parent who called forth light and whose word made the sky-roof and divided night from day, next created Rangi (Space) and Papa (Matter). These two were the Sky Father and Earth Mother of Maori mythology.

Rangi and Papa begot the eleven great gods. Their twin offspring, Rongo and Tane, produced the food plants and creeping vines. Rongo became the god of vegetation and growth, and hence of agriculture. Tane produced the forests and birds and insects, and was the promoter of life. It was Tane who raised the low-hanging sky from the earth so the gods could stand up and things could grow. Rangi's grief at being thus separated from Papa so touched his pity that he dressed his father in a robe of stars. But still today Rangi's tears fall on the Earth Mother in the form of dew and Papa's sighs rise to Rangi in the form of mist.

Others of the gods produced the four winds and the rains. Earthquake, too, was one of the eleven sons of Rangi and Papa. He still keeps trying to get away from his mother, and his struggles cause the earth to shake.

The ninth son of Rangi and Papa was Tu, the warrior god, whose offspring are living men, "like us," the Maori say, "unafraid."

173

The tenth child was Tangaroa, the sea god, who takes care of fishermen. Tangaroa was father of the legendary Maui, culture hero of all the Polynesian peoples from Hawaii to New Zealand. New Zealand itself is called the Fish of Maui, for Maui is said to have fished up the land out of the sea. Maui is the hero who beat the hurrying sun over the head with a club, thus persuading him to move more slowly and prolong daylight. He brought fire to earth for mankind, and later died in his search for immortality for the people.

The last child of Rangi and Papa was named Pu-whakarere-i-waho, who produced death and injustice.

Tiki was the name of the first man. Some of the Maori say that Tane made him out of red clay, and some say that the god Tiki made the first man in his own image and named him Tiki for himself.

The little *hei-tikis* of the Maori people are grotesque little human figures carved of nephrite or whalebone and worn on a string around the neck. They are embryo-shaped and worn as fertility charms to bring many babies: that is, many men (*tikis*). The word *hei-tiki* means "tied-on tiki."

This is the Maori creation myth, condensed from and based on a document given to Lieut.-Col. W. E. Gudgeon, government resident for many years at Raratongo, New Zealand, translated by Hare Hongi of one of the Maru-tuahu tribes, and published in the *Journal of the Polynesian Society* 16:113-119 (1907). Articles (on the gods named in the myth) in the *Standard Dictionary of Folklore, Mythology, and Legend* have also been used. The concept of Io as supreme god seems to be limited to certain Maori tribes in North Island, but the rest of the myth is widespread.

IN MELANESIA

MELANESIA is roughly divided into three big areas. The first is New Guinea, one of the earth's hugest islands. The second is a curving chain of archipelagoes, which takes in the Bismarck Archipelago, the Solomon Islands, Santa Cruz and Banks Islands, New Hebrides, the Loyalties, and New Caledonia. The Fiji Islands comprise the third.

There are many creation stories throughout Melanesia. Concepts and stories differ from area to area, and from island to island, and even one small island may have different myths about the origin of the world or mankind.

The Papuan Keraki people of southwestern New Guinea say that the first people came out of a palm tree. Gainji was the Great Creator. He heard a babble of voices inside the palm and liberated the babblers in groups that spoke the same language. This explains the existence of different languages in the world. The Papuan Kiwai people (also New Guinea) have a creator named Marunogere, who gave people their first pig and first coconut tree, and built the first men's house for the religious rituals.

In the second area there are many stories about a wise, beneficent hero-god who is accompanied by a foolish, blundering brother, or several brothers. In the New Hebrides, for instance, the people tell about two Tagaros, twin culture heroes, one very wise, one foolish. Tagaro, the wise, created foods and useful artifacts for man; the other Tagaro created useless things and hindered or spoiled his brother's work to such an extent that he had to be tricked out of this world.

The people of San Cristobal have Agunua, who made the sea and the land, caused storms, and created men and one woman. Agunua caused the rains to fall in order to quench his own thirst. He too had a brother companion to whom he gave a yam. He told the brother to plant it, and from this primeval yam grew all the banana and almond trees, coconuts, and other fruits. But one time the brother burnt up a mess of yams, thus causing some plants to be inedible forever.

Banks Islanders have the creative Qat with his stupid brother Marawa, and ten others who had to be told what to do.

In the Fiji Islands the people say that in the beginning there was no land—no land but the land of the gods. There was only the sea and the sea was everywhere. The sky which was over the sea touched nothing but the edge of the sea. There was no bright day, no night. A dim twilight lay upon the water.

The land of the gods was an island, as it is now. No one knows where it is for sure, but the old people say it floats in the sea on the edge of the world at the very point of sunrise. The people of Kandavu say they have seen it on the horizon lighted by the sun, but when they head their canoes toward it, it disappears before they can arrive.

Ndengei was the Great God of Fiji, the serpent-shaped creator, who made all things and taught the Fijians how to build canoes. He was chief of the *Kalou-Vu,* the "root-gods" of Fiji. They are called the root-gods because they were there first, the truly Fijian gods, rooted in Fiji before there was any Polynesian or European influence.

At night Ndengei went into a cave on the hill of Kauvandra to sleep. This is a hill in Great Fiji. When he closed his eyes it was dark over the islands and people called it "Night." If he turned over in his sleep, the people said "Earthquake." And when Ndengei opened his eyes again, it was day, and the people said "Work," and built their canoes.

Ndengei now pays no attention to the people, but because of his great hunger he accepts offerings of fruits of all kinds, vegetables, and pigs, and turtles. The people pray to him for good harvests.

His son Rokomautu created the land. He scooped it up out of the bottom of the ocean in great handfuls and piled it up in piles here and there. These are the Fiji Islands.

This survey is based on material in R. B. Dixon's *Oceanic Mythology* and L. Fison's *Tales from Old Fiji,* as well as on the article "Melanesian mythology" and the entry "Kalou-Va," both in the *Standard Dictionary of Folklore, Mythology, and Legend.*

177

QAT

WHEN the Melanesian people in the Banks Islands see the shadow of a cloud moving swiftly over the face of the sea, they say "There flies Qat." Qat created men and pigs and food, they say, and if a pig runs into the house, they drive it out with the words 'Qat says stay outside."

Qat himself was born on Vanna Lava (one of the Banks Islands), the very center of the world, and of what happened before that there is no tale.

Qat was born from the bursting of a stone. His mother was a great stone that split in two and Qat came forth and named himself. He had no father; but he had eleven brothers. They all lived together in the village of Alo Sepere. And there the mother, Qatgoro, can still be seen, the huge stone that gave birth to Qat.

Qat began to make things right away: men and pigs and plants and stones—or whatever he thought up.

He made mankind from the wood of the dracaena tree. He carved the arms and legs and torsos separately, and the heads and ears and eyes, and the fingers and toes, then fitted them all together, slowly and carefully. He made six figures and when they were finished he set about giving them life.

He stood the man-images up in a row and danced before them. After a while they moved a little—weakly, stiffly—but they moved. When Qat saw that, he began to beat upon his drum.

Soon the wonderful rhythmic magic of the drum filled

the air. The figures began to move a little more, slowly and carefully at first, in time with each drum beat, then faster and faster, until they too were dancing the life dance of the drum. At last they were able to stand and walk and run by themselves.

Then Qat divided the six figures into men and women: three men and three women, so that each man had a wife, each woman had a husband.

Qat's brother, Marawa, came along while Qat was doing all this and watched. Marawa was the stupid one; he spoiled everything he tried to do. He thought he would like to create some people too.

So Marawa cut down a tree—another kind of tree, the *tavisoviso*—and from it carved six figures, as Qat had done. He set them up and danced before them and beat the drum to give the figures life, just as he had seen Qat do. But as soon as he saw them move, he dug a pit and buried them, and went away and left them.

In about a week he remembered them, and went and scraped the earth away. They were rotten. They stank, and Marawa had to leave them buried in the earth. This was the beginning of death in the world.

When Qat first made the pigs he made them to stand upright and walk on two legs. But his brothers all laughed. They pointed and laughed and said they looked just like men! So to save the pigs from ridicule, Qat shortened their forearms and fixed them to walk on all fours, as they do now.

Thus Qat made men and pigs. He made food plants, and canoes, and many other things. But he did not know how to make darkness. It was light in the world all the time, without dimness or dark or rest.

179

The eleven brothers did not like the world this way.

"Look here, Qat! It's too light," they said, or "There's nothing but light all the time, Qat!", or "Qat, can't you do something?"

Qat searched around and one day he heard that there was something called *night* over at Vava in the Torres Islands. So he tied up a pig and put it in his canoe and set sail across the water for Vava.

There he bought (in exchange for a pig) a piece of night (*qong*) from Qong, Night, who dwelt in that place. After that there were pigs in the Torres Islands, they say. Another story says Qat never went to the Torres Islands at all, but sailed out over the sea to the far edge of the sky, where Night himself touched him over the eyes and gave him black eyebrows and taught him sleep.

Some say this can't be true because there are pigs in the Torres Islands and none in the sky.

At any rate, Qat returned to Vanna Lava bearing night and bringing also various birds and fowls to make a clamor when it was time for day.

Qat showed the brothers how to construct beds of coca fronds and spread them on the floor and how to lie down for rest.

The brothers looked out and saw the sun moving down the west.

"It is departing," they cried to Qat. "Will it come back?"

"What is happening is called *night*," Qat told them.

Then he let loose the night.

"What is spreading and covering the sky?" cried the brothers.

"This is night," said Qat. "Lie down and keep quiet."

The brothers lay down, and in the dark they felt strange and dreamy; their eyes grew heavy and closed.

"Are we dying?" said the brothers.

"This is sleep," said Qat.

Only the birds knew how long the night should last; so when the night had lasted as long as the night should last, the cock crowed and the birds began to call and answer.

Qat then took a piece of red obsidian for a knife and cut a hole in the night. The first light that showed through was red, and soon all the light the night had covered shone through once again. The brothers opened their eyes and started the work of the day.

This is the way mankind lives now: day—sleep—day.

Rewritten from R. H. Codrington: *The Melanesians: Studies in Their Anthropology and Folklore,* 156-158.

ABOUT THE LITTLE ISLANDS

MICRONESIA, a world of little islands, is still the least known of all the areas in the South Pacific. It includes the Caroline Islands, the Gilberts, the Marshall Islands, and the Marianas: somewhere between 700 and 1,000 islands, coral reefs, and atolls. There is no one creation story. Not only do the myths differ from group to group, but from island to island.

The Ifaluk people of the central Carolines, for instance, have a creator god named Aluelap, but it is his grandson, Wolphat, who features in most of the stories. Wolphat is a trickster, and when a tale is told about some particularly outrageous prank of his, the people laugh and explain tolerantly, ". . . but he was not a person, just a god." One day when he tilted back his head to drink from a coconut he saw his grandfather in the sky and went at once to visit him. There Aluelap taught the young Wolphat everything.

On the island of Truk in the Carolines the story is that Ligoububfanu, daughter of the sky god, gave birth to mankind and animals and later to coconuts and grain. The face of her first child can still be seen on the coconut.

The people of the Radak chain in the Marshalls say that the first living beings were two worms, Wulleb and Lejman, living together in a shell. Together they worked and raised the top shell to make the sky; the lower shell became the earth. Wulleb still exists, the people say, on Eb Island to the westward. And there the birds congregate once a year to pluck their feathers for his tribute and to feed him fish.

In the Gilberts the people mention Nareau, the Elder, the preexistent one, who commanded sand and water to bear children. Among these children were Nareau, the Younger, who said to the others, "Rise up now. Live and be men."

But they could not. The sky pressed down so low over the earth that they could not stand up. Then Eel raised the sky and arched it. And then Nareau, the Younger, killed Nareau, his father, and took out his eyes to be the sun and moon in the sky, and set his spine on end in the island of Samoa, to be the ancestral tree for all mankind. All mankind was born of this tree. The tree is named Kai-ni-tiku-aba.

The people on Nauru say that at first there was nothing but the sea. And Areop-Enap lived in a mussel shell in the sea. It was dark in the bottom of the sea, dark inside the shell; he could see nothing. But by feeling

183

around in the dark, he discovered that a big snail and a small snail occupied the shell with him. With his great power Areop-Enap changed the little snail into the moon and placed it in the upper part of the shell.

He looked around in the dim light and saw a worm. At once he set the worm to work separating the upper and lower parts of the shell. It worked hard and finally got the upper and lower shells apart, to become the sky and the earth. But when the work was finished the worm died of exhaustion, and his sweat dripped into the lower shell and made the salty sea.

Areop-Enap placed the big snail in the sky to be the sun, and then created men out of stones to support the sky. Then Areop-Enap walked around in the world to see what it was like.

This brief survey is based on the faithful recording of Melford E. Spiro in his "Some Ifaluk Myths and Folktales," *Journal of American Folklore* 64:289f. (1951); on the article "Micronesian mythology" by Katharine Luomala, and the entry "Areop-Enap," both in the *Standard Dictionary of Folklore, Mythology, and Legend.*

Mmmmmm

LONG AGO when all was water, Lowa, the uncreated, was alone in the sea. "*Mmmmmm*," he said, and islands rose out of the water. "*Mmmmmm*," he said, and reefs and sandbanks were created.

"*Mmmmmm*," he said, and plants appeared. Again he uttered the creative word, and birds came into being.

Then Lowa made four gods for the four directions in the sky and a white gull to fly encircling the heavens forever.

Iroijdrilik was the one who was to preside over the west, the land of Eb, and to be in charge of life and increase and all living things. Lokomran was put in charge of the east. The people say he is the one "who twists the daybreak." Lorok was given the south and told to regulate the winds. Lalilikian is the north-man, who brings death.

Then Lowa sent a man into the world whose name is forgotten. This man put all the islands in a basket (a big *kilok* woven of coconut leaves) and started to put them in order. He put the Carolines to the westward, where they are today, and arranged the Marshalls in two long chains in their proper order. One island fell out of the basket, but he did not stop to put it straight. This is Namorik, which is still out of line. The last two to be put in their places were Jaluit and Ebon. Then he threw away the basket. It floated here and there in the ocean, and then stopped and became the island named Kili. It is named this for the basket (*kilok*) which formed it.

When Lowa looked down and saw that the world was now ready, he sent two tattooers into the islands to mark every living thing with its own mark. And every plant and fish and bird, every animal, every man and woman bears these special marks today.

At that time only one small, sandy island had any coconut trees. And the people named this island Bikini. *Bok* means sand; *ni* means coconut. Bikini was the sandy place of the coconut.

Sometimes Iroijdrilik, the god of the west whose country is named Eb, sends his son to the island of Ebon to see how the people are faring. Ebon is named for Eb, and therefore Iroijdrilik takes special care of it. When the black tern flies over Ebon, crying out, the people believe this is a promise of plenty. The god remembers the island, and this is why, they say, Ebon produces more food than the other islands.

This story, told by the people of the Ralik chain of the Marshall Islands, is based on the recording by William H. Davenport and published in his article "Marshallese Folklore Types," *Journal of American Folklore* 66:219f. (1953), and in the account given by Katharine Luomala in her "Micronesian mythology" in the *Standard Dictionary of Folklore, Mythology, and Legend*.

DREAM TIME

ALMOST ALL of the primitive peoples of Australia think of the world as always already there, but they have stories about a mythical dream time. This was the time of the first people, the Ancestors. The Aranda call that time *alchera*, dream time; the Murngin people of Arnhem Land call it *bamum;* and *tjukur* is what the tribes of the Great Western Desert say.

In the beginning at first, in the dream time, the Ancestors emerged from the earth somewhere "to the north" and wandered the dream path, stopping now and then at *billabongs* (water holes) now called "story places," because here they stopped to create food plants, or certain animals, or to fix up the landscape to their liking.

The Wati Kutjara, or Two Men, of the Great Western Desert peoples, stepped into the dream time out of the vague northwest and began their "walkabout."

They were brothers; one was stupid and blundering; the other was creative and full of vim. Their totem was the iguana, and so they were sometimes called Men Iguana. Sometimes they themselves went around in the shape of iguanas.

They created water holes for themselves, and animals to live on the earth and drink from the water holes. They made birds and all the edible plants. They made rock shelters for wanderers to rest in. They made the boomerang and gave it the magic whereby it returns to the hand of the thrower. They made spears to hurl at kangaroos. And they made the bull-roarer for men to use later in their religious ceremonies; and they devised the special headdresses which the people still wear in their religious rituals.

Everywhere in Australia the bull-roarer is regarded as a wonderful and mysterious thing. Its voice is the voice of some powerful spirit or god. Its voice protects young boys from evil in almost all the tribes, and among the Urabunna of Central Australia the sound of the bull-roarer is said to be the voice of the spirit which changes young boys into men. It gives them courage and power.

As the Wati Kutjara traveled northward they stopped to create fruit trees. They waited for the fruits to ripen and piled them in a great heap. Then they pounded them into fruitcakes on flat stones. The people today still do this, saying, "We do as did Wati Kutjara."

At a place named Kulardu the Two Men forgot to pick up their spears, and walked away without them. Here wonderful trees grew up from the spears and today the people make spears from this kind of tree because it is the toughest for fine spears.

The Wati Kutjara killed the first thief and turned him into stone; and thus they brought the first death into the world also, before they returned to their home in the sky.

HELLO, I'M A LIZARD

THE northern Aranda people of Australia say that the old gods made the first man in the form of a lizard. But he was so stiff that he could hardly move, and he could not walk at all.

So he lay there in the sun. The sun was warm and the lizard grew warm, and stretched. After a while he thought of himself lying there in the sun, and he looked at himself, and said, "Hello! I'm a lizard!"

So he lay there in the sun, warming himself, and after a while he saw another lizard lying on the ground beside him.

"Hello! There's another lizard!" he said.

After a while this lizard, too, grew warm and stretched. "Just like me!" said the first lizard.

So the two lizards lay there, warming themselves, and after a while there were a lot of lizards lying in the sun. They were very stiff at first, but the sun warmed them, and one by one they stretched.

Then after a while, when they were thoroughly warmed and limber, all the lizards stood up. Their tails dropped off and they walked away like men. All except one. One of them had died. Thus happened the first life and the first death.

"So that is the way it is going to be," said the first man.

And now when they saw that the lizards had become men, the two old gods who made them changed themselves into lizards and ran off.

The Aranda therefore revere the lizard. No one would kill a lizard.

LIZARD'S PEOPLE

THE Pindupi and Jumu tribes of Australia say that
Pupula created the first human ancestors. The word
pupula means lizard in their language. Pupula (Lizard)
was their man-shaper.

The first people were already there when Pupula came
along, but they were smooth all over and they lay with
their fists doubled up on their chests and with their knees
bent and legs pulled up against their stomachs: exactly
the position in which newborn babies lie today.

When Pupula came along and saw them like this he
thought he would fix them up. So he gave each one a
nose, two eyes, and two ears, one mouth, and two elbows,
and very carefully cut their toes and fingers apart. Then
when they were able to walk and pick things up, he
showed them how to make fire and taught them all their
laws and ceremonies.

The western Aranda people tell almost the same story.
Their Creator-Lizard is named Manger-kunger-kunja.
He drew the first people out of the ocean and cut them
into shape with a stone knife. Then he cut a mouth in

the face, then two eyes, two ear-holes, and with two shells made lobes for the ears.

Then Munger showed the people how to make fire. He showed them how to make spears and how to use them, how to spear kangaroos.

He gave the people boomerangs and put the magic in them which makes them return to the hand of the thrower; and he showed the people how to throw them and how to receive them back in the hand without being hurt themselves.

Then Munger made a wooden *churinga* (a bull-roarer) and put his own voice in it, so that it was a sacred thing. And he showed the people how to make them, each one with his own totem symbol, and how to use them in the religious ceremonies.

Thus the western Aranda received both themselves and their learning from the Lizard, and still today hold all lizards in reverence. No Aranda would kill a lizard; if he did, the sky would fall down on the earth.

The Australian Dieri creator, called First Ancestor, first made mankind in the shape of little black lizards. He divided their hands and feet into fingers and toes and poked his finger into their faces to make eyes and mouth, and pinched up a nose in the middle. Then he stood them up, expecting them to walk, but they could not stay upright because of the long tails. So he cut the tails off, and then they were men and walked away.

These three Australian myths are based on Katharine Luomala's article "Australian aboriginal mythology" in the *Standard Dictionary of Folklore, Mythology, and Legend* (see also article "lizard"), and on material in Geza Roheim's *Eternal Ones of the Dream.*

VIII

Siberia

THAT IS ALL

THERE IS a small Eskimo village named Unisak on a
little cape which juts out into the lower waters of Bering
Strait from the Chuckchee Peninsula, Siberia. The Eskimos of that village tell this story about the creation of
the world:

Raven and his wife created the world, they say. They
made the cape of Unisak from the bill of an eider-duck.
They made Alaska out of a long knife (the kind the
Eskimos wear in their belts), then they made the island
of Imalik from the button which fastens the knife scab-
bard around a man's hip. (Imalik is a little round island
right in Bering Strait about halfway between Siberia

and Alaska. On English maps it is one of the three Dio-
mede Islands.) Then they made the reindeer out of their
own hair and dogs from their fingernails.

That is all.

ON KUKULIK ISLAND (which is St. Laurence Island, lying offshore from Unisak), the Eskimos living
there today say that Creator made the shoreline of Unisak first of all when he was creating the world, then he
made the country of the Russians, and then the land of
the Americans.

Then he was tired and thought he would rest. The
sun was just setting, and he said, "Well, there is still
time for me to make something small," so he reached
down to the bottom of the sea and picked up a handful
of sand. He squeezed it hard and squeezed all the water
out of it. (There is a little village on the westernmost
point of St. Laurence Island named Cibukak, which
means "wrung out.")

As soon as the water had all dripped out and the sand
was dry, Creator laid it down in front of himself—a low,
long mound of sand. After that he picked up pebbles
and amused himself by placing them here and there.
These became people.

"You will catch your food out of the water," he told
them. And so the people ate seaweeds and fished and
hunted walrus and seal for their meat.

One day a certain young man of the island set out on
a journey to the sky, to ask the Sun for reindeer for the
people.

"No," said the Sun, "the reindeer are not for the island
of Kukulik; but I will give you something else."

Sun picked up two handfuls of pebbles. "Here," he said, "go home and throw these in the water."

The young man did as he was told. He returned to Kukulik and strewed the pebbles in the water. At once they turned into many whales. Thus the Eskimos of Kukulik received their own special source of livelihood—the whales. They are whaling there today.

That is all.

Retold from two fragments collected by Waldemar Bogoras: *The Eskimos of Siberia,* Publications of the Jesup North Pacific Expedition, Vol. 8.

MAN, REINDEER, AND DOG

THERE WERE two of them, Raven and Creator. "Make a man," said Raven.

So Creator created a man—a big, hairy man with large teeth and long, strong arms. He ran on all fours and he could run faster than any living creature, and he could talk. He would run after any animal and catch it and eat it. He did not know how to cook.

"He'll destroy every living thing!" cried Creator. "We'd better destroy *him.*"

"No need," said Raven. "Just make him slower and make him walk with a staff."

So together they fixed him. They made his arms shorter, so that he could run on two legs only. The hair fell off his body and he had to wear clothes. And for running the man helped himself along with a long birch staff, just as the Chuckchee do today.

But he got hungry; he could not catch his food.

"Make reindeer," said Raven.

198

So Creator created the reindeer; out of moss and earth and larch and willow he made them. And the next day men became reindeer herders.

"Make dogs," said Raven.

So Creator created dogs; he made them out of wood. And the next day men were driving dogs.

By this time there were many people, living along the rivers. They bred the reindeer and drove the dogs.

One family moved away and left a dog behind. Raven took this dog and carried him home. So now Raven also had a dog.

This is a Reindeer Chuckchee story told to Waldemar Bogoras on the Molonda River in 1895 and retold from his "Chuckchee Tales," *Journal of American Folklore* 41:305 (1928).

THE FUR COAT

IN THE BEGINNING there was Sombov, the god, and nothing else but water. Sombov looked upon the water and saw the bird Anghir swimming on the waves.

"Dive," he said, "and bring up earth."

So Anghir disappeared into the deep and came up with black earth in his beak and red clay in the toenails on his feet. Sombov took the black earth and tossed it around here and there and the earth began to take its shape and grass and trees began to grow upon it.

Then from the red clay Sombov made a man and a woman, covered with wool. He sat looking at the shapes and was thinking in his mind about giving life to them and giving each a soul. But he would have to go to heaven for the soul. So he made a dog, a naked dog, and set him to watch the lifeless figures.

The dog sat and watched the shapes and shivered in the wind a little now and then. Along came Shiktur, the evil one, the destroyer, and wanted to see the people.

"No!" said the dog. "Do not come near."

200

"Cold, shivering one, I will cover you with fur—just let me come near enough to *look* at the wonders."

So the dog allowed Shiktur to approach and Shiktur spat on the people and soiled them. And all the dog got out of the deal was a covering of coarse rough hair.

When Sombov came back and saw what had happened, he cursed the dog. "You shall shiver in the cold just the same," he said; "you shall gnaw bones for food, and be beaten by those you love."

Then Sombov shaved the wool off of the people, except here and there where Shiktur had not spat upon them. So man comes naked into the world from that time forth.

Another version of this story says that when the creator returned to his handiwork and saw that the evil one had spat upon them, he turned them inside out, so that now people are all wet and slimy inside.

This story is very common among the peoples of Siberia. The Black Tatars tell it one way, other southern Siberian Turkic peoples tell it another. The Buriats have the first-told version; and it is known with varying detail among the Yakuts, the Cheremis, the Votjaks, and the Mordvins. The Samoyeds say that man and dog were created naked together; the dog grew hair from the devil's stroking him.

This story is based on material presented by Demetrius Klementz in his article "Buriats" in the *Encyclopedia of Religion and Ethics,* III: 11-12.

IX
Ainu

SLUSH

IN THE BEGINNING the world was slush, for the waters and the mud were all stirred in together. All was silence; there was no sound. It was cold. There were no birds in the air. There was no living thing.

At last the Creator made a little wagtail and sent him down from his far place in the sky.

"Produce the earth," he said.

The bird flew down over the black waters and the dismal swamp. He did not know what to do. He did not know how to begin.

He fluttered the water with his wings and splashed it here and there. He ran up and down in the slush with his feet and tried to trample it into firmness. He beat on it with his tail, beating it down. After a long time of this treading and tail-wagging a few dry places began to appear in the big ocean which now surrounds them—the islands of the Ainu. The Ainu word for earth is *moshiri*, floating land, and the wagtail is reverenced.

WHENCE MAN?

THE AINU themselves say "whence Ainu?" for the word *ainu* means man. Did the first Ainu fall out of the sky? Did he spring forth from a tree? Did the first Ainu grow up out of the earth? Or was the first ancestor the polar bear, "the big white dog of heaven"? The Ainu themselves think this must be the answer. The Ainu are a very hairy people, and how else would they come to be covered with hair?

Some of the old men used to tell a story about Okikurumi who came down from the sky with his wife Turesh and dwelt on the top of a mountain. The creator sent Okikurumi to them, they say, with "bundles of benefits" which he opened for the people, and then disappeared. Others say that the son of Okikurumi and Turesh, named Wariunekuru, was the first ancestor.

Wariunekuru dwelt among the people many years and taught them how to make cloth, how to hunt and fish, how to make poisons, and how to make the big spring-bow and set it in the trails to catch game. The Ainu pantheon includes a creator god, the sun, the moon, and the bear. They look upon the bear as ancestor and god who beneficently provides them with meat.

The Ainu are the aboriginal people of Japan, now dwelling only in the northernmost islands. This story and the one before it, "Slush," are based on material in G. Batchelor: *The Ainu and Their Folklore,* and his "Notes on the Ainu" in *Transactions of the Asiatic Society of Japan,* Vol. 10 (1882).

X
Classic

WHEN ABOVE

The ancient Babylonian epic of creation is called *Enuma Elish* from the first two words with which it begins: *Enuma elish,* When above. . . . It has been called the oldest story in the world, for the ancient Sumerians knew it centuries before it was written down.

The *Enuma Elish* was written in the Akkadian language (an ancient Semitic language which was probably the only language spoken in Mesopotamia by the end of the third millennium B.C.). It exists in cuneiform writing on a series of baked clay tablets which were dug up in Nineveh in 1873, less than a hundred years ago. But it was written on those clay tablets (incised into the soft clay) about 2500 B.C., and the myth itself goes back— how many ages behind that, nobody knows.

The beautiful poem begins:

When above no sky had yet been mentioned
And below no earth was named ...

THEN in the beginning there was only the great primeval water, named Apsu, the begetter, and chaos, named Tiamat, the deep, the mother, the dragon of the deep, the salt sea, the deep itself, who gave birth to the gods.

There was no sky, no earth before the mingling of these two. Before any little swampy place existed, before any little island took shape, from the mingling of the primeval waters and the waters of chaos, Apsu and Tiamat, two gods, were born.

Two gods were born and were named. Lachmu and Lachamu were the names. This pair, formed of the silt of the two great waters, grew and increased through the ages. Two gods were born of Lachmu and Lachamu and were named. Anshar and Kishar were the names. These two arose from the primeval silt to be the two horizons. Anshar, the male, was to encircle the sky, and Kishar, the female, was to encircle the earth. They are there now, these two great circles.

Ages passed and of them Anu was born, Anu, the sky. Time passed (*year unto year* the poem says) and then came Nudimmut, the earth. This is another name for Enki, lord of the earth, later known as Ea or Ea-Enki. Anshar shaped them into roundness like himself: Anu, the circling dome of sky, encircles the round earth.

This story is the most natural story in the world. In ancient Mesopotamia this IS the way it happened, and the people saw Babylonia continuing to be created before their eyes, the very way it began. Southern Baby-

212

lonia was itself the silt deposited between two great rivers: the Tigris and the Euphrates. And still today this land (now approximately Iraq) is advancing into the Gulf of Persia at the rate of 116 feet a year. The ancient city of Eridu, which the Sumerians thought was the first city on earth, was a seaport 6000 years ago. Today it lies more than a hundred miles inland.

Thus the gods were born, and took it upon themselves to dance for joy. And the running to and fro disturbed Tiamat. Her labors were over. She longed only to sink into herself. She longed to sleep. Neither could Apsu stand the noise. He tried to quiet the merry crew but the clamor and uproar continued. So he went to consult with Tiamat.

"I get no rest," he said, "all day, all night this to-do continues. I cannot sleep."

Tiamat said nothing.

"I will destroy them," said Apsu, "and then we two may rest."

This news reached the gods and they were confounded. They did not know how to save themselves.

Of them all only Ea was wise enough to think up something. To outwit the primeval deep, Ea sang a sacred spell over the waters of Apsu, so that Apsu slept. And with the holy words the universe swung into motion, as it is today. The primeval waters never rose again, and Ea, as earth, dwelt upon the sleeping waters.

Then on the earth was born Marduk, son of Ea, tall, beautiful, terrible, strong, fearless, four-eyed, four-eared, and lips ablaze. He grew up among the gods, increasing daily in strength and subtlety.

The primeval waters slept but chaos did not sleep.

213

The hosts of chaos grew apace. Tiamat was moved to avenge Apsu and prepared to destroy the gods. Prowling monsters she gathered together, serpents and great dragons filled with poison, crowned with fire, and so deadly that the sight of them would kill the beholder. Tiamat made Kingu, her second husband, leader of this ugly horde, and gave him power over the fate of the universe.

When Ea learned that the powers of annihilation were amassing, he sat in silence till his heart emptied itself of fear. Then he went to Anshar, his father, and revealed the plot of Tiamat.

"You overcame Apsu," said Anshar. "Do the same with Tiamat."

So Ea went forth against Tiamat, but he knew no sacred spell that would conquer chaos. There was no word of power more powerful than Tiamat.

"You go," Anshar then said to Anu. "Speak the word to make Tiamat subside." But Anu had no words more powerful than Tiamat.

"Call Marduk," then said Anshar. "Call Ea's strong young son."

Marduk was delighted with the prospect of vanquishing Tiamat. He would go, he would win, he said, "but first give me your word, if I conquer Tiamat and save the gods, that you will proclaim me supreme among you."

So the gods assembled at a great feast in Nippur in central Babylonia. They ate the rich food and drank the strong wine and forgot their fears and sang for joy and promised Marduk everything. They gave him the kingship and power: power of weapon and power of word. And to test the power they laid out a garment and said to Marduk: "With a word destroy the garment, and with a word restore it." So Marduk spoke—and there was no garment; he spoke again, and there lay the garment in their midst. And the gods said, "Thou art king."

So Marduk prepared for battle. He made a great bow that arched across the heavens; he took lightning for his arrows, and the arrows flashed ahead of him as he went. He made a great net to ensnare Tiamat, and the four winds held the corners of it. So riding the tempest, followed by seven terrible storms, and with the floods at his fingertips, Marduk advanced against the powers of chaos. And the gods watched.

When Kingu and the hosts of chaos saw him coming, terror consumed them. But Tiamat knew no fear and stood unconcerned, awaiting battle.

Marduk flung the net and encircled the great dragon of the deep. Tiamat opened her jaws to swallow him and the winds rushed into her open mouth and swelled the great belly till it burst. When the armies and monsters saw this, they turned and tried to escape; but Marduk caught them all in the huge net and they were destroyed.

Marduk then cut Tiamat's body in two and lifted up half of it to be the sky, and there (just as Ea had made his dwelling upon Apsu) did Marduk establish his dwelling on that half of Tiamat which was the sky. The other half of Tiamat became the rolling oceans which wash the edges of the lands.

Thus did Marduk win for the restless living gods the battle against chaos and nonmotion. In the sky which he had lifted up he placed the stars and the swinging planets. He made the moon to travel through the night and measure time.

Then, because Kingu was judged to have incited Tiamat against the gods, they placed on him the war guilt, and bound him so that he could not move and killed him. Blood from his arteries poured out upon the earth, and from this blood the first man was created.

> *Man shall be formed*
> *Lullu shall be his name*

sang the gods. "Man shall toil for the gods" they said, "and the gods shall be free."

And so it is. Man toils and serves his gods.

Every year on New Year's Day in ancient Babylon, the *Enuma Elish* was recited in the temple of the god Marduk, and the religious drama of the creation of the world and Marduk's victory over Tiamat was enacted— for the day the world was created was the first New Year's Day.

THE FIRST TIME

THE FIRST TIME is what the ancient Egyptians called the moment of creation, and one story says that the first sound ever made was the honking of a wild goose over the vast primeval sea. This goose was the sun god who flew out from an egg which lay on the primeval hillock as it rose from the waters of chaos. Thus began the universe out of the great primeval waters, with that first moment of time, the first dry spot of earth, the first god, the first sound.

The most ancient and primitive story begins with the waters of chaos, Nun, the primeval ocean, and the god who created himself, the sun god. The oldest of the stories says that his name was Atum, which means "everything" and "nothing." The *Book of the Dead* says his name was Atum when he was alone in Nun, and his name was Ra when he began to rule creation.

217

Before Atum came into being there was no heaven, no earth, no creature, no little place for any creature to put its foot. Only the waters of chaos existed, until Atum rose out of the waters and became the god. *Out of the abyss I came to be*—are the words of the creator in one of the ancient hymns—*But there was no place to stand*—. So Atum created a little mound of dry earth to stand on, and this was the beginning of the world.

This bit of dry earth, the primeval hillock, is represented in old Egyptian writings by the hieroglyph

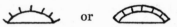 or

which represents the sun on the little mound at the moment of that first time. It was the sign for the word *khay*, which means "to shine forth" or "to appear in glory." It was also used for the appearance of the sun every morning. The primeval mound of creation was represented by a little high place in every Egyptian temple and the pyramids also symbolized it.

Thus Atum, the sun god, or Atum-Ra, arose from the waters of chaos, uncreated, and *became*. He first made the little primeval hill of mud on which to stand, and then he created Shu (air) and Tefnut (moisture). Shu and Tefnut then produced Geb (the earth god) and Nut (the sky goddess). And this pair, Geb and Nut, produced the gods Osiris and Isis, Set and Nephthys, from whom all gods and men are descended, and their children are many today upon the earth.

But each great city in Egypt had its own version of the story of creation; the tales existed side by side, and the Egyptians accepted them all as obviously true and

218

valid. In the city of Heliopolis, the city of the sun, this was the story: the story of Atum or Atum-Ra.

Twenty-five miles from Heliopolis was the city of Memphis where Ptah was the creator-god. Ptah represented the creative power of the earth. Ptah "thought in his heart" everything that was to be, and when he uttered his thought, this was the creative word, and whatever he said came into existence. Ptah uttered "Shu" and Shu was born; he said "Tefnut" and Tefnut came into being. Shu (air) and Tefnut (moisture), united and produced the sky and the earth. Nut, the sky-mother, is usually depicted in ancient Egyptian art, star-spangled, and bending over Geb, the earth. She is usually seen supported on the two uplifted hands of Shu. To them were born the four great Egyptian gods, Osiris and Isis, Set and Nephthys, the four ancestors of all the gods and all mankind. The Egyptians made no sharp distinction between gods and men. All received life from the same source.

In the island city of Elephantine in the Nile, Khnum was the creator-god. Khnum was always shown with a ram's head and probably represented belief in the power of animals to create life, i.e. to reproduce their kind. And Khnum's story is that he made an egg out of clay and from this created the world, and then shaped mankind on his potter's wheel.

At Thebes, Amon, the wind god, called the Hidden One, was supreme. He was the mysterious breather who passed unseen across the world and gave man breath and life. Thus the power of wind (Amon) and sun (Ra) were thought to be one, and Amon too became Amon-Ra.

These stories were not contradictory in Egyptian

219

thinking. That life might begin on the little primeval mound was not mere conjecture. Every year the Nile flooded its banks and spread across the land, and as the waters subsided, little hillocks of slimy mud rose up, teeming with miniscule life in the hot sun. Here was the source of life; this was how it must have been. The power of the sun to generate life is something every man can see with his own eyes, as the sun warms and quickens seed and germ in the earth. The power of the earth to generate life was equally obvious, for plants and grasses spring from the nourishing soil, and insects and reptiles crawl out of the eggs entrusted to the fostering mud. The power of animals to create life is proved with the cry of every little lamb or kid or kitten in its first moment of birth. It was all the same life force; the creator gods all partook of the sun's creative power and were all named Ra (the sun), as Atum or Atum-Ra, Khnum or Khnum-Ra, or Amon or Amon-Ra.

LORD OF CREATURES

THERE ARE so many creation stories in Hindu mythology that it is impossible to say that any one of them
is *the* creation myth of India. Four Vedas comprise the
sacred literature of Hinduism, and of these the *Rig-Veda*
is the original and most ancient one.

In the *Rig-Veda* one of the creation stories begins with
the rolling primeval waters, in which evolved a golden
egg. And from this egg came the lord of all being who
made heaven and earth and bestowed life and breath on
the creatures. Prajāpati, lord and father of creatures,
was the title given to this life-giving deity.

Later Hindu myth says that Brahma was born from
this golden egg, which shone with a light as dazzling as
the sun. Brahma lay in the egg for one year, and then
with the power of his thinking thought the shell into

two parts. The upper shell became the heavens and the lower shell the earth. But the name of Brahma is not mentioned in the Vedas.

Another Vedic story says that Kaśyapa, the Old Tortoise Man, created the universe and fathered all living beings. (The word *kaśyapa* means tortoise.) He himself was born of Time, self-born, the Vedas say, and Prajāpati, lord of creatures, was one of his titles also.

But the famous Hymn of Creation from the *Rig-Veda* says, "Who knows whence comes this creation?" In the beginning there was no air, no sky. "Was the water there?" says the hymn. There was no death then; there was no life; but something breathless breathed, and that was all. There was darkness; there was chaos. But warmth was a power, and out of that breath and that warmth evolved "the primal seed and germ of spirit." But who knows and who can say when it first came into being? Even that He who originated this creation—perhaps He knows, perhaps He knows it not.

In the *Vishnu Purāna*, a collection of legends of about 600 A.D., Vishnu is the Prajāpati, creator and lord of creatures, who saved the young Mother Earth from destruction.

The earth came into being of itself, the story says, and lay lightly floating on the water of the abyss. It was time for warm blood to run in the veins of the animals; it was time for the animals to romp on the face of the earth; it was time for man to appear.

But just as Time dawned (this our present age) and just as flowers opened in the grasses of the world, the great serpent of the cosmic sea grabbed the floating earth and dragged her to the bottom of the abyss.

Vishnu, Lord of the Universe, took on himself then the form of a monstrous boar. (Vishnu in the shape of the boar was named Varāha.) He dove into the waters; with gleaming tusk and four sharp hoofs he tore and trampled the cosmic serpent and saved the lovely earth. On his huge tusks he raised her and brought her back to the surface of the sea. This is one of the episodes which gave Vishnu his title of Preserver and Restorer and Maintainer of the World.

SOMETHING FROM NOTHING

AT FIRST there was nothing. Time passed and nothing became something. Time passed and something split in two: the two were male and female. These two produced two more, and these two produced P'an Ku, the first being, the Great Man, the Creator.

Thus begins one version of the Chinese creation myth. Another says that first there was the great cosmic egg. Inside the egg was Chaos, and floating in Chaos was P'an Ku, the Undeveloped, the divine Embryo. And P'an Ku burst out of the egg, four times larger than any

224

man today, with an adze in his hand (or a hammer and chisel) with which he fashioned the world. Two great horns grew out of his head (the horned head is always the symbol of supernatural power in China); two long tusks grew from his upper jaw, and he was covered with hair.

P'an Ku went to work at once, mightily, to put the world in order. He chiseled the land and sky apart. He piled up the mountains on the earth and dug the valleys deep, and made courses for the rivers.

High above ride the sun and moon and stars in the sky where P'an Ku placed them; below roll the four seas. He taught mankind to build boats and showed him how to throw bridges over rivers, and he told them the secrets of the precious stones.

One story says that the world was never finished until P'an Ku died. Only his death could perfect the universe: from his skull was shaped the dome of the sky, and from his flesh was formed the soil of the fields; from his bones came the rocks, from his blood the rivers and seas; from his hair came all vegetation. His breath was the wind; his voice made thunder; his right eye became the moon, his left eye, the sun. From his saliva or sweat came rain. And from the vermin which covered his body came forth mankind.

A more local legend says that when P'an Ku wept his tears became the Yellow River, and when he died his body formed the five sacred mountains of China. T'ai Mountain, in the east, rose from his head; Sung Mountain, in the center, from his body; Heng Mountain of the north rose from his right arm, Heng Mountain of the

225

south from his left; Hua Mountain in the west grew out of his feet.

It is said that P'an Ku's image can still be seen in a cave cherished by the Miao tribe in the Mountains of Kuangsi, and that along with the image of P'an Ku stand also images of the three great sovereigns who followed him: the Lord of Heaven, the Lord of Earth, and the Lord of Man.

ANCIENT MATTERS

This is the creation story of Japan as told in the *Kojiki*, the oldest chronicle of the Japanese people, published in 712 A.D.

THERE WAS CHAOS—but who could say what shape? There was no shape; nothing moved; there was no name. Yet in this void, earth and sky cracked apart, and between heaven and earth something became. Something became a god and the name of the god was the One-Who-Stands-Forever-Over-The-World, Kuni-toko-tachi, that Lord-in-the-center-of-the-sky.

227

With him came two others: Tako-mi-musubi, the High-producing-wondrous-god, and Kami-mi-musubi, the Divine-producing-wondrous-goddess. They were born alone and uncreated. And after them came six more: companion gods of mud and seeds and germination.

Time and ferment worked together, and time passed. At last were born the wonderful heavenly pair, Izanagi and Izanami. To them the gods of heaven said, "Go find this drifting land." And they put into the hands of Izanagi a long jewelled spear.

So these two, Izanagi and Izanami, male and female, walked slowly from the sky across the Bridge of Heaven (which was perhaps the rainbow) and standing on it looked over the edge—down, down—into the primeval ocean.

"Is the earth there?" they said. No answer came.

Izanagi then reached down with the flashing spear of heaven and plunged it into the waters. He stirred the waters till they seethed. And when he drew back the spear, the brine that dripped from its tip fell back into the ocean and became an island. This was Onogoro-jima, the Island of Onogoro, which means self-congealed. It was a tiny place, but when Izanagi and Izanami saw it lying lovely in the sea, they walked down the Bridge of Heaven and placed their feet upon it. And they set up the spear in the middle of it to be the pillar of the world. Here on this small spot of earth they became man and wife. Their first child was misshapen and they threw it into the sea, where it became the little island named Ahaji.

After that were born the eight beautiful islands of Japan, Land-of-the-Eight-Great-Islands. Their next

offspring were the rivers and the waterfalls; then were born the mountains and the forests and the fields. Then the wind was born; the Lord-of-Long-Breath, who blew away the mists which hung over the world, so that the world could be seen. After this came all the tiny islands of the Japanese archipelago, and the offspring of Izanagi and Izanami were beautiful and many.

Izanami's last child was the god of fire. At his birth she was burned up with fever and died and left this earth and went to the Land of Gloom, the underworld. Broken-hearted, Izanagi went in search of her, and finally came to the place. All would have been well and he could have taken Izanami back to the world, except for his impatience.

"Lead the way and I shall follow," said Izanami joyfully. "But don't look, DON'T LOOK!"

But Izanagi could not wait. He wanted to reassure himself with one look at her beautiful face. So he lighted a little torch in that dark pit and saw only the horrifying, decaying corpse of Izanami.

He turned and ran. And Izanami in disappointment and distress and anger ran after him as he fled and called upon all the demons and hags and furies of the pit to help her catch him. Izanagi ran in terror. He threw behind him the wild grapes and bamboo shoots that grew on the comb in his hair, and the demons stopped long enough to eat the luscious fruits. At last he escaped by throwing down a peach, and the pursuing thunders picked it up and were silenced. But Izanami followed to the very edge of the pass into this world, where Izanagi plugged up the hole with a rock before she could get out.

230

Izanami cried out from behind the rock, "I shall cause 1000 of your people to die every day!"

And Izanagi said, "Then I shall give birth to 1500 every day." And thus it is that death has never quite been able to catch up with life.

Then Izanagi, wishing to wash away the horridness of death, went into a stream and bathed, and the stain of everything he had touched in the underworld was washed away.

From this purifying bath were born many things, both good and evil. From his left eye was born Ama-terasu, the sun goddess, Heaven-Illuminating-Deity. From his right eye sprang the moon, Tsuki-go-mi, Guardian of the Night. And from his nostrils came Susa-no-wo, the storm god, the Swift-Impetuous-Deity.

Ama-terasu and Susa-no-wo personified the antagonism of Izanagi and Izanami, the age-old struggle between life and death. Ama-terasu was the goddess of light and life, promoter of germination, irrigation, and good crops and the civilized order. Susa-no-wo delighted in destroying the irrigation ditches in the rice fields, and promoted disorder, darkness, and death.

Once they decided to make up their quarrels and live in peace; they exchanged gifts and drank together from the heavenly well. But Susa-no-wo could not stand peace very long. He began to act up again and just for fun destroyed his sister's rice fields and filled up the irrigation ditches. Then for a prank he broke a hole in the roof of heaven where Ama-terasu and her weaving maids sat at work, and flung through it "a heavenly piebald horse" which he had skinned. Ama-terasu could not stand this at all. She hid in a cave, and nothing anyone

231

could say or do would make her come out. She would
not even show her face.

There was no light in the world. Dark lay over the
earth. And evil things ran around loose in the dark.

Eight million gods gathered together in front of the
cave and begged her to come out. But Ama-terasu just
said, "No!"

So they put up a tree, the *sakaki* tree and hung it with
jewels and colored ribbons and hung a shining mirror
on it. But the lovely Ama-terasu would not come out of
the cave. Next they brought eight million cocks to crow
before the cave, but the sun would not come out. They
offered her mirrors; they offered her jewelled swords.
No. Ama-terasu did not want them. Gorgeous raiment
was brought to the place, but she would not even peep
out and look. The sun remained hidden in the cave and
the world was dark.

Then the little goddess Uzume stepped up on a flat
upside-down tub before the crowd and began to dance.
She was a fat girl, with a happy sly look, and the dance
she performed was a comic obscene dance.

The gods laughed. For all their dismay at the loss of
the sun, the gods laughed. Uzume continued to dance
and the gods laughed so hard and so loud that the sound
of laughter filled the earth and all the space beyond. Inside the cave Ama-terasu heard the laughing. What was
going on, she wondered. What in the world was going
on outside? The laughter poured around the cave and
shook the earth.

She thought she would *just peek!*

But the minute she opened one crack to peek out, one
of the gods pulled her out by the hand.

"Look!" he said, and showed her her own face in a mirror. Ama-terasu was so astonished and beguiled by her own bright reflection that she forgot her determination to hide from the world. Thus sun and warmth and life came back into the world.

OUT OF CHAOS

IN GREEK classical myth there is no creator hewing out a universe. First of all came Chaos and before that— nothing. But man's mind cannot think "nothing," so Chaos contained the seeds of all things that *were to be*.

Out of Chaos slowly rose the sleeping earth, for earth was one of the things that *was to be*. And Earth, while she slept, gave birth to Uranus. Uranus later became identified with the sky. He showered his mother, the earth, with rain, so that trees shot up, flowers bloomed, grass grew everywhere, and animals and birds were born in the forests and grasslands. Lakes filled up and rivers flowed down to the seas.

Later the Greeks gave Mother Earth the name of Ge or Gæa, and called Uranus the Sky Father. Sky-Father (Uranus) and Earth-Mother (Ge) were parents of the hundred-handed giants and the one-eyed Cyclopes, who built the great ancient walls and won fame as smiths. The seven Titans were also children of Uranus and Ge, but Uranus found them troublesome and thrust them back into the earth and imprisoned them deep within.

Ge resented this and persuaded Cronus, the youngest of them, to rebel against his father. And she gave him a sickle with a sharp obsidian blade for a weapon. Armed with this sickle Cronus led the Titans against Uranus and overcame him. Thus Cronus himself became the ruler of the universe.

A late myth says that the Titan Prometheus created mankind out of clay and water, and brought fire to them from heaven in a fennel stalk. But Plato tells another story, saying that mankind grew up on the face of the earth, spontaneously, from the seeds of life in the earth itself, like the birds and animals.

These first people, who sprang from the earth, were the men of the Golden Age during the reign of Cronus. There was no sickness or old age among them and no fear of death. When death came they gladly slept. They ate acorns from the oaks; honey flowed from the trees for them; they drank goats' milk, and laughed often.

The Silver Age came next. These people were farmers and learned to make bread, but they offered none of it to the gods, so Zeus, son of Cronus, and now high god, destroyed them.

The third age of mankind was the Bronze Age, when men made and carried weapons of bronze and made wars and killed each other off.

The Iron Age is the present age of the world and the people are not any more admirable. They make wartools out of iron and they wage cruel and unjust wars.

In the *Iliad* Homer mentions the old god Oceanus as encircling the world: the worldwide concept of the primeval waters (by another name) from which sprang all life.

235

MIDDANGEARD

Here is the story of the universe as conceived by the ancient Northmen of Iceland, Scandinavia, and what is now northern Germany. It is a magnificent, though grim, murky, and severe concept of cold and icy frost and fog. Ginnungagap, the gaping void, was so real to these people that in the eleventh century when the Northmen began to explore the unknown western ocean, they gave the name Ginnungagap to the cold, fog-hidden sea between Greenland and America.

THERE LAY the cold and fathomless abyss in the center of the universe, the yawning gap, Ginnungagap,

236

halfway between Niflheim and Muspellheim. Niflheim was the northern region of cold and mist and dark. *Nifl* was the old Icelandic word for fog; *heim* means home. Muspellheim lay to the south, the land of fire and flame.

All the rivers of the universe poured into the yawning gap, and as they spilled the utter cold transformed the waters to blocks of ice which fell eternally into the bottomless chasm with endless thundering sound.

Hot sparks from Muspellheim flew into this void, and, falling on the ice, raised a hoary mist which gathered into frost and amassed, layer on layer. This frost through the ages slowly came to life and became the monstrous Ymir, the first living being, "the rime-cold giant," asleep in the gap. Audhumbla nourished him. Audhumbla, the cow of the abyss, whose name means nourisher, fed him with four great streams of milk. She herself was nourished by the frost, and as she licked the salty ice a living one took shape, first head, then trunk, then arms and legs, then features.

And while Audhumbla licked, the being breathed. And this was Buri, first ancestor of the gods. And Buri's son, born unmothered, was Borr, who later became the father of Odin, mightiest of all the northern gods.

Later Odin with his two brothers, Vili and Ve, killed the giant Ymir and shaped this our earth from his flesh. This was Midgard, the middle earth between heaven and hell, in Old English called *Middangeard* (*middan,* middle, and *geard,* yard, which meant garden; later it came to mean field, and by extension, earth).

Then the gods rolled Ymir's huge body back into the yawning gap. And Ymir's blood became the ocean. His bones formed the mountains and the rocks. From his hair

237

grew the trees of the earth and the grasses and all plants.

His great skull formed the dome of the sky, supported by four famous dwarfs named Nordr (north), Austr (east), Sudr (south), and Westr (west). A million sparks from Muspellheim were caught inside the skull and can be seen today moving across it, as sun and moon and countless stars. Ymir's brain still broods over the earth in the form of dark fog and heavy low-lying clouds.

From the maggots that crawled in the dead flesh of Ymir the gods created the dwarfs. They lived underground and fashioned gorgeous jewels and swords out of the metals of the earth, and feared the light of day lest they be turned to stone. They had great wisdom and one of them, named Dvalin, invented the runes which have preserved all the lore of the north.

The Midgard Serpent is the great serpent that encircles the world. His name is Jörmungandr. He was the offspring of two of the early gods, and Odin threw him in the sea when he was a little snake, lest he harm mankind. He grew and grew until he encircled the world. He holds the tip of his tail in his mouth, and if he wiggles a little, this world has storms and earthquakes.

Later Odin and his brothers, Vili and Ve, decided to make people for the world. They created the first man from a living ash tree and named him Ask, for the tree from which he was made. Odin gave him his life and soul. Vili gave him the five senses and the power of motion, and Ve made the blood run red in his veins. They created the first woman in the same way, from a living elm tree and named her Embla. Odin endowed her with life and soul; Vili gave her motion and senses; Ve gave her her blood.

238

BARLEY GROW

This is Finland's ancient story of how the world began, retold from the *Kalevala*, Runes 1 and 2.

AT FIRST there was nothing but air and water. The blue space stretched far forever and under it rolled the blue waters, deep and cold.

Air had a daughter, named Ilmatar, who wandered lonely through the never-ending blue. But she tired of emptiness and one day sank down to rest upon the ocean's face.

239

The seas foamed over her; the waves tossed her to and fro. The wind blew around her; the sea woke her out of dreaming and planted the germ of life within her. For seven hundred years Ilmatar swam and floated in the far-extending sea, tossed by storm and wave, driven before the wind, tortured with loneliness and the longing to create life.

One day she lay floating in the quiet sea, just floating gently with one knee cocked up comfortably out of the water. And she saw something moving in the upper space. She had never seen *anything* before and she watched and wondered.

It was a bird—a beautiful duck, a teal—flying, swooping, east, west, south, looking for a place to rest. But nothing existed but space and water. There was no resting place.

Soon the teal came flying over Ilmatar, quick and curious. It saw the knee sticking up out of the water. It swooped past, then turned and flew back, hovered a moment, flew off, flew back, and then lighted on this white thing—a haven so miraculously given.

Ilmatar lay still. A sharp joy consumed her but she did not stir for fear the slightest movement would make the beautiful, living bird fly away. But the bird rested on the knee and there laid seven eggs. Six were gold; the seventh egg was iron. The teal sat quietly over the eggs to keep them warm. Ilmatar could feel the eggs grow warm. The bird sat there day after day; the eggs grew warmer and warmer—then hot. Her knee felt hot, then hotter and hotter; she thought it was burning.

Finally she could not endure it. She gave a quick jerk and pulled the knee down into the cool water. The bird

240

flew away and the eggs rolled into the water and sank down into the soft ooze on the ocean floor.

In time a wonderful change took place. From the cracked egg's lower shell, the solid earth was formed. From the upper shell the sky arched itself over sea and land. Out of the yolk the sun slipped into the sky. From the white, the moon and stars were formed and took their places. Centuries went by and still Ilmatar floated on the face of the ocean. The sun shown and dazzled the sea by day; the new moon's soft light touched the night waters.

Then Ilmatar began the work of creation. Wherever she pointed, jutting headlands, capes, and cliffs took form. Wherever her feet touched, she made holes and deep pools for the fish. She dived and shaped the ocean depths. She swept her hand over the land and made the long and level shores; wherever her head touched shore, a round bay took shape. She made the rocks in the ocean, the unseen reefs and ledges, and the little islands that dot the sea. The continents spread across the world, and rivers ran between the clefts of the hills.

Then Ilmatar gave birth to the sea's child, Väinä-möinen. He was born in the ocean and swam for seven years before his knees scraped on the sand of a treeless island. He crawled ashore on his hands and knees, shaking the foam from his hair and eyes. He put his foot upon the earth and stood. The first man on earth stood up and saw the moon in the heavens and the shining stars of the Great Bear over his head.

"Oh, Great Bear, lend counsel," he said.

The years went by. Väinämöinen wandered on the barren island. No tree grew anywhere.

Then one day a youth appeared, bearing seeds, and Väinämöinen told him to scatter the seeds across the land. Thickly the boy scattered them and the trees sprang forth: pine trees grew on the hills, fir trees on the little knolls; birch trees and alders sprang up in the valleys and heather covered the sandy stretches. Cherry trees and willows grew in the damp earth. Juniper spread its blue-green arms across the rocks, loaded with berries. The rowan flourished and oaks pushed up their tiny sprouts beside the rivers.

All sprouted and grew tall and strong and bore fruit except the oak. Again and again the little acorns were planted, but the oak was slow to rise. But it reached down its roots at last and took hold in the earth. It grew and spread. The leaves were thick; the branches grew and forked; the top reached into the clouds and stopped their passing. The great oak grew so huge and thick that it hid the sun and moon. It shadowed the waters so that the fish were gloomy in the dark sea.

And Väinämöinen cried out, "Who will fell the oak?" He prayed to his mother in the sea to send some power to fell it and restore sunshine to the world.

She heard him and sent ashore a tiny man clothed in copper, with a copper ax stuck in his belt. Väinämöinen thought the puny creature would never be able to cut down the tremendous oak; but even as he doubted, the man grew huge before his eyes, lifted his ax, and with three strokes brought the oak crashing.

Once again the sun lighted the world; the forests grew green and splendid; and thrushes sang in the trees. Everything flourished—except barley. Väinämöinen walked around and worried. Seven grains of barley he

242

found at the sea's edge and went to sow them. But the barley would not grow.

A titmouse mocked him from a tree. "Barley will not grow in a forest," he said. "Barley will not grow in an untilled field. Barley will not grow until fire has burned the land."

So Väinämöinen cleared a place for the barley. With keen-sharp ax he leveled the lovely trees, but spared one birch for the birds to rest in.

The greatest of all birds of the earth saw this and came to look.

"Why is the birch not fallen?" asked the eagle.

"That the birds of the air may rest," said Väinämöinen.

"Thou art wise, Väinämöinen," the eagle said, and flew into a tree and with his beak struck fire.

The flames rose and roared across the forest and the trees lay in ashes.

Thus the word of the titmouse was fulfilled, and Väinämöinen took the seven barley seeds in his hand to sow them.

"Now I stoop the seeds to scatter," he chanted. "Old Earth Mother, let the tender blade spring up; let the stalks grow up and lengthen; let the ears grow big, by thousands, and may the stalks rustle."

Then when the seeds lay in the earth, Väinämöinen prayed for rain, and the rain came. The sprouting grain drank and flourished and when Väinämöinen looked in the morning, he found the barley growing. And thus the first cereal plant known or used by man was established in the world.

XI

Bibliography and Artist's References

BIBLIOGRAPHY

J. de Angulu: "Pomo Creation Myths," *Journal of American Folklore* 48:203-262 (1935)

Marius Barbeau: "How Raven Stole the Sun," *Transactions of the Royal Society of Canada* 38. Ottawa, 1944

———: *Haida Myths,* Bulletin 127, Anthropological Series 32, National Museum of Canada. Ottawa, 1953

J. Batchelor: "Notes on the Ainu," *Transactions of the Asiatic Society of Japan,* vol. 10. Yokohama, 1882

———: *The Ainu and Their Folklore,* 582f. London, 1901

Martha Warren Beckwith: *Kumulipo.* Chicago, 1951

Ruth Benedict: *Zuni Mythology,* vol. 1. New York, 1935

Junius Bird: "The Alacaluf" in *Handbook of the South American Indians,* vol. 1. Washington, 1946.

W. H. I. Bleek and L. C. Lloyd: *Specimens of Bushman Folklore.* London, 1911

Franz Boas: *The Central Eskimo,* Bureau of American Ethnology Report 6. Washington, 1888

———: *Folktales of Salishan and Sahaptin Tribes,* Memoir 11, American Folklore Society. New York, 1917

Waldemar Bogoras: *The Eskimos of Siberia,* Publications of the Jesup North Pacific Expedition, vol. 8, pt. 3. Leiden and New York, 1913

———: "Chuckchee Tales," *Journal of American Folklore* 41: 305 (1928)

A. C. Bouquet: *Sacred Books of the World.* Baltimore, 1954

Ruth Bunzel: *Zuni Origin Myths,* Bureau of American Ethnology Report 47. Washington, 1929-1930

S. W. Bushell: *Chinese Art,* 2 vols. London, 1924

Henry Callaway: *The Religious System of the Amazula.* London, 1870 (Publications of the Folk-Lore Society xv, 1884.)

Codex Vaticanus 3773 (Codex Vaticanus B) An Old Mexican Pictorial Manuscript in the Vatican Library. Elucidated by Eduard Seler. Berlin and London, 1902-1903

R. H. Codrington: *The Melanesians.* Oxford, 1891

Eduard Conzemius: *Ethnological Survey of the Miskito and Sumu Indians of Honduras and Nicaragua,* Bureau of American Ethnology Bulletin 106. Washington, 1932

John M. Cooper: "The Ona" in *Handbook of the South American Indians,* vol. 1, 107f. Washington, 1946

————: "The Yahgan," *ibid.,* 81f.

Jeremiah Curtin and J. B. N. Hewitt: *Seneca Fiction, Legends, and Myths,* Bureau of American Ethnology Report 32. Washington, 1910-1911

William H. Davenport: "Marshallese Folklore Types," *Journal of American Folklore* 66:219f (1953)

Arundel Del Re: *Creation Myths of the Formosan Natives.* Tokyo, 1951

R. B. Dixon: "Oceanic," *Mythology of All Races,* vol. 9. Boston, 1916

John Dowson: *Classical Dictionary of Hindu Mythology,* 8th ed. London, 1953

C. G. Du Bois: "Mythology of the Mission Indians," *Journal of American Folklore* 17:183-188 (1904)

A. P. Elkin and R. and C. Berndt: *Art in Arnhem Land.* Chicago, 1950

John C. Ferguson: "Chinese Mythology," *Mythology of All Races,* vol. 8. Boston, 1928

Lorimor Fison: *Tales from Old Fiji.* London, 1904

Henri Frankfort: *Ancient Egyptian Religion.* New York, 1948

248

Henri and H. A. Frankfort, John A. Wilson, and Thorkild Jacobsen: *Before Philosophy*. Harmondsworth, 1949

Moses Gaster: *Rumanian Bird and Beast Stories*. London, 1915

Irving Goodman: "Cosmological Beliefs of the Cubeo Indians," *Journal of American Folklore* 53:242-247 (1940)

Robert Graves: *The Greek Myths*, 2 vols. Baltimore, 1955

Handbook of the South American Indians, Bureau of American Ethnology Bulletin 143, 6 vols. Washington, 1946-1950

J. Hastings: *Encyclopedia of Religion and Ethics*. New York, 1908-1927

Melville J. Herskovits: *Dahomey: An Ancient West African Kingdom*, vol. 2, 289-292. New York, 1938

"Horizon of the Universe," *Time*, March 14, 1955

Sir James Jeans: *The Mysterious Universe*. Cambridge, England, 1930

Kalevala. Translated by W. F. Kirby. London and New York, 1951

A. L. Kroeber: *Handbook of the Indians of California*, Bureau of American Ethnology Bulletin 78. Washington, 1925

Kojiki: Record of Ancient Matters. Translated by B. H. Chamberlain. Transactions of the Asiatic Society of Japan, vol. 10, Supplement. Yokohama, 1883

Adolf N. Krug: "Bulu Tales from Kamerun, West Africa," *Journal of American Folklore* 25:111 (1912)

Maria Leach and Jerome Fried: *Standard Dictionary of Folklore, Mythology, and Legend*, 2 vols. New York, 1949-1950

Samuel Kirkland Lothrop: *Indians of Tierra del Fuego*, Museum of the American Indian, Heye Foundation. New York, 1928

Robert H. Lowie: *Myths and Traditions of the Crow Indians*, Anthropological Papers, American Museum of Natural History 25. New York, 1918

Duff Macdonald: *Africana: The Heart of Heathen Africa.*
London, Edinburgh, Aberdeen, 1882

D. A. Mackenzie: *Myths of China and Japan.* London, 1923,
260*f*, 247*f*

Sir Clements Markham: *The Incas of Peru.* London, 1910

W. Max Müller: "Egyptian Mythology," *Mythology of All
Races,* vol. 12. Boston, 1918

"Non-Commonsense Cosmos," *Time,* September 24, 1954

Morris Edward Opler: *Myths and Tales of the Jicarilla Apache
Indians,* Memoir 31, American Folklore Society. New
York, 1938

Oxford Classical Dictionary. Oxford, 1949

Popol Vuh: Sacred Book of the Ancient Quiché-Maya. English version by Delia Goetz and Sylvanus G. Morley
from the Spanish translation of Adrián Recinos. Nor-
man, Oklahoma, 1952

Paul Radin: *The Story of the American Indian.* New York,
1944

————: *Origin Myth of the Medicine Rite (Three Versions),*
Memoir 3, International Journal of American Linguis-
tics (1950)

Geza Roheim: *The Eternal Ones of the Dream, a Psychoana-
lytical Interpretation of Australian Myth and Ritual.*
New York, 1945

Morris Siegel: "The Creation Myth and Acculturation in Acatán, Guatemala," *Journal of American Folklore* 56:120-
126 (1943)

S. C. Simms: *Traditions of the Crows,* Field Columbian Museum Publications 85. Chicago, 1903

W. M. Smart: *The Origin of the Earth.* Baltimore, 1955.

Melford E. Spiro: "Some Ifaluk Myths and Folktales," *Journal of American Folklore* 64:289*f*. (1951)

John R. Swanton: *Haida Texts—Masset Dialect,* Publications
of the Jesup North Pacific Expedition, vol. 10, pt. 2.
Leiden and New York, 1908

————: *Myths and Tales of the Southeastern Indians,* Bureau of American Ethnology Bulletin 88. Washington, 1929

P. Amaury Talbot: *In the Shadow of the Bush.* London, 1912

Stith Thompson: *Tales of the North American Indians.* Cambridge, Mass., 1929

————: *Motif-Index of Folk-Literature,* 6 vols., (Indiana University Studies 96-112). Bloomington, 1932-36

E. Torday and T. A. Joyce: *Les Boshongo,* Annales du Musée du Congo Belge, Ethnographie, Anthropologie, Serie 4, t. 2. Brussels, 1910

G. C. Vaillant: *The Aztecs of Mexico.* Harmondsworth, 1950

Heinrich Zimmer: *Myths and Symbols in Indian Art and Civilization,* Bollingen Series 6. New York, 1946

ARTIST'S REFERENCES

Leonard Adam: *Primitive Art*. Harmondsworth, 1954
American Museum of Natural History, Anthropological Collections. New York
The Animal Kingdom, 3 vols. New York, 1954
Marius Barbeau: *Haida Myths*, Bulletin 127, Anthropological Series 32, National Museum of Canada. Ottawa, 1953
Boston Museum of Fine Arts, Far Eastern Collections. Boston
Codex Fejérvary-Mayer: An Old Mexican Picture Manuscript in the Liverpool Public Museum, le Duc de Loubat, photographic edition. Paris, 1901
G. H. Collingwood and W. P. Brush: *Knowing Your Trees*, 9th ed., American Forestry Association. Washington, 1947
Arundel Del Re: *Creation Myths of the Formosan Natives*. Tokyo, 1951
F. C. Douglas and R. d'Harnoncourt: *Indian Art of the United States*, Museum of Modern Art. New York, 1941
Encyclopaedia Britannica: article on "Chinese Sculpture"
J. B. Griffin: *Archaeology of the Eastern United States*. Chicago, 1952
T. Heyerdahl: *American Indians in the Pacific*. London, 1952
F. W. Hodge: *Handbook of American Indians North of Mexico*, 2 vols. Washington, 1907-1910
A. L. Kroeber: *Handbook of the Indians of California*, Bureau of American Ethnology Bulletin 78. Washington, 1925

252

Gaston Maspéro: *The Dawn of Civilization.* New York, 1894

M. Mead: "The Maoris and Their Arts," American Museum of Natural History Guide Leaflet 71. New York, 1928

Paul Radin and James J. Sweeney: *African Folk Tales and Sculpture,* Bollingen Series 32. New York, 1952

M. E. Sadler: *Arts of West Africa.* London, 1935

H. J. Spinden: *Ancient Civilizations of Mexico and Central America,* American Museum of Natural History Handbook Series #3, 3rd ed. New York, 1928

Matilda Coxe Stevenson: *The Zuni Indians, Their Mythology, Esoteric Fraternities and Ceremonies,* Bureau of American Ethnology Report 23. Washington, 1901-02

G. C. Vaillant: *The Aztecs of Mexico.* New York, 1944